FACTOR ANALYSIS AS A STATISTICAL METHOD

BUTTERWORTHS MATHEMATICAL TEXTS

CONSULTANT EDITOR: P. T. LANDSBERG

PUBLISHED

Theory of Integration
Ralph Henstock

IN PREPARATION

Optimal Trajectories for Space Navigation
D. F. Lawden

Theory of Satellite Orbits in an Atmosphere
D. King-Hele

FACTOR ANALYSIS AS A STATISTICAL METHOD

D. N. LAWLEY, M.A., D.Sc.
Mathematical Institute, University of Edinburgh

and

A. E. MAXWELL, M.A., Ph.D.
Institute of Psychiatry, University of London

LONDON
BUTTERWORTHS
1963

ENGLAND:	BUTTERWORTH & CO. (PUBLISHERS) LTD. LONDON: 88 Kingsway, W.C.2
AFRICA:	BUTTERWORTH & CO. (AFRICA) LTD. DURBAN: 33/35 Beach Grove
AUSTRALIA:	BUTTERWORTH & CO. (AUSTRALIA) LTD. SYDNEY: 6–8 O'Connell Street MELBOURNE: 473 Bourke Street BRISBANE: 240 Queen Street
CANADA:	BUTTERWORTH & CO. (CANADA) LTD. TORONTO: 1367 Danforth Avenue, 6
NEW ZEALAND:	BUTTERWORTH & CO. (NEW ZEALAND) LTD. WELLINGTON: 49/51 Ballance Street AUCKLAND: 35 High Street
U.S.A.:	BUTTERWORTH INC. WASHINGTON, D.C.: 7235 Wisconsin Avenue, 14

Suggested U.D.C. Number: 519·241·6

Made and printed by offset in Great Britain by
William Clowes and Sons Ltd, London and Beccles

PREFACE

We are indebted to Messrs Butterworth for inviting us to write this book. While doing so we had two aims primarily in mind. The first was to present the statistical theory of factor analysis, as it has been developed so far, in a concise form which would enable mathematical statisticians to discover readily what the subject is about. The second aim was to illustrate the theory by some carefully chosen examples so that the ever increasing number of research workers who use factor analysis would be enabled to do so in a more rigorous way than has been the case in the past.

In factor analysis, even more than in other branches of multivariate analysis, the amount of calculation involved is great, but with the advent of electronic computers this obstacle has to a large extent been overcome. Our thanks are due to Mr W. L. B. Nixon and Mrs G. Gallagher, of the London University Computer Unit, who helped us by writing computer programmes for two of the more laborious iterative processes. We also thank Miss Nona Hemsley for assistance with other aspects of the calculations.

Scientists often come under censure for their misuse of language, and any literary merit that the book may possess should be attributed largely to our wives.

D.N.L.
A.E.M.

CONTENTS

1

THE SCOPE OF FACTOR ANALYSIS

1.1. Introduction

Factor analysis is that branch of multivariate analysis which deals with the internal structure of matrices of covariances and correlations. Initially it was developed mainly by psychologists, with Spearman, Thomson, Thurstone and Burt as the most prominent pioneers, and was primarily concerned with hypotheses about the organization of mental ability suggested by an examination of matrices of correlation between cognitive test variates. The early work in this difficult field gave rise to protracted controversies on the psychological side which damped for a time the interest shown by mathematicians in the statistical problems involved, and the subject became the black sheep of statistical theory. But 'factor analysis', as Bartlett (1953, p. 23) has remarked, 'must be regarded as a natural and inevitable development in the analysis of the correlated sets of test scores and other variables with which psychologists have had to deal', and gradually (see references at the end of the chapter) the statistical theory of the subject was built up. Today factor analysis is the most widely used of multivariate techniques, though not always appropriately, as Hotelling (1957) has pointed out. Also its use has been facilitated by the advent of electronic computers and is spreading to disciplines other than psychology: to economics, botany, biology as well as to the social sciences; so that an attempt to set out the statistical theory of the subject is desirable.

In this introductory chapter the problems with which factor analysis deals and the models it employs will be surveyed in a general way, while in succeeding chapters specific topics will be elaborated. Owing to limitations of space, the illustrative examples employed in the book have had to be kept small and so are not altogether typical of factorial studies, in which matrices of correlations containing forty or more variates are not uncommon, but they are adequate to illustrate the theory of the subject. The examples are mainly psychological, as most of the published work is in this field, but the general principles of factor analysis can readily be generalized and applied in other fields.

1.2. Factor models

When analysing the structure of covariance (or correlation) matrices two approaches, which formally resemble each other to some extent but have rather different aims, are currently employed. One is principal component analysis following Pearson (1901) and Hotelling (1933), while the other is factor analysis and stems from the work of Spearman (1904, 1926). In the interest of clarity it is advisable to distinguish between these two approaches, and, while this book is primarily concerned with factor analysis, the principal component method will also be described. The latter is a relatively straightforward method of 'breaking down' a covariance or correlation matrix into a set of orthogonal components or axes equal in number to the number of variates concerned. These correspond to the latent roots and accompanying latent vectors (see Appendix) of the matrix. The method has the property that the roots are extracted in descending order of magnitude, which is important if only a few of the components are to be used for summarizing the data. The vectors are mutually orthogonal, and the components derived from them are uncorrelated. Although a few components may extract a large percentage of the total variance of the variates, all components are required to reproduce the correlations between the variates exactly. When the principal component method is employed no hypothesis need be made about the variates. They need not even be random variates, though in practice their observed values are usually regarded as a sample from some population.

In contrast to the principal component method the aim in factor analysis is to account for, or 'explain', the matrix of covariances by a minimum, or at least a small number of hypothetical variates or 'factors'. Put simply in correlational terms, the first question asked is whether significant correlation exists, that is whether the correlation matrix differs significantly from the identity matrix. If the experimenter is satisfied that this is so he then asks whether a random variate f_1 exists such that the partial correlations between pairs of variates are zero after the effect of f_1 has been removed. If the correlation matrix is still unexplained he enquires whether two random variates, f_1 and f_2, exist so that the partial correlations between pairs of variates are zero after the effects of both these variates have been removed; and so on (Howe, 1955, p. 8 *et seq.*). In a sense then it can be said that whereas a principal component analysis is *variance*-orientated, a factor analysis is *covariance*-orientated.

The aims of the two methods of analysis can also be stated directly in terms of the observed variates and the derived components or factors. Let the p observed variates be denoted by $x_1, x_2, \ldots, x_p$. In component analysis an orthogonal transformation is applied to them to produce a new set of uncorrelated variates, $y_1, y_2, \ldots, y_p$. These are chosen such that y_1 has maximum variance, y_2 has maximum variance subject to being uncorrelated with y_1, and so on. Again no hypothesis need be made regarding the x's.

In factor analysis on the other hand, the basic assumption is that

$$x_i = \sum_{r=1}^{k} l_{ir} f_r + e_i \quad (i = 1, 2, \ldots, p), \tag{1.1}$$

where f_r is the rth common factor, k is specified, and e_i is a residual representing sources of variation affecting only the variate x_i. The p random variates e_i are supposed to be independent of one another and also to be independent of the k variates f_r. We shall initially suppose that the latter are uncorrelated, but later we shall consider the case where they are correlated. Without loss of generality we may take the variance of each f_r to be unity. The variance of e_i is denoted by v_i. All the means are supposed to be zero. The coefficient l_{ir} is usually termed either the loading of the rth factor in the ith variate or the loading of the ith variate on the rth factor. The quantities l_{ir}, and usually also the v_i, are taken to be unknown parameters which have to be estimated. Here it may be mentioned that attempts have been made to treat the individual values of the f's also as parameters, but this raises difficulties, a serious one being that when the sample size tends to infinity so also does the number of parameters (Whittle, 1953). This approach will be ignored in this book.

It is clear that eqs (1.1) are not capable of direct verification since the p variates x_i are expressed in terms of $(p+k)$ other variates which are not observable. However, the equations imply a hypothesis, which can be tested, concerning the variances and covariances of the x's (see Chapter 2).

A further contrast between principal component and factor analysis, to which Bartlett (1953, p. 32 *et seq.*) has drawn attention, must also be mentioned. The former method is by definition linear and additive and no question of a hypothesis arises, but the latter includes what he calls a *hypothesis of linearity* which, though it might be expected to work as a first approximation even if it were untrue, would lead us to reject the linear model postulated in eqs (1.1) if the evidence demanded it. Since correlation is essentially concerned with linear relationships it is not capable of dealing with this point, and Bartlett briefly indicates how the basic factor equations would have to be amended to include, as a second approximation, second order and product terms of the postulated factors to improve the adequacy of the model. In the amended form the product terms especially would be of interest and the equation

$$x_i = l_{i1}f_1 + l_{i2}f_2 + e_i, \tag{1.2}$$

which involves just two factors, would then become

$$x_i = l_{i1}f_1 + l_{i2}f_2 + l_{i3}f_3 + e_i, \tag{1.3}$$

where $f_3 = f_1 f_2$. While the details of this more elaborate formulation have still to be worked out, mention of it serves to remind us of the assumptions of linearity implied in eqs (1.1), and to emphasize the contrast between factor analysis and the empirical nature of component analysis.

1.3. Factor concepts and factor rotation

In the previous paragraphs an attempt has been made to clarify the distinction between principal component analysis and factor analysis. An important further point concerning certain invariance properties under changes of scale in the variates, which factor loadings possess and component weights do not possess, will be mentioned in Chapter 2. In either case the components or factors obtained are, on their face value, weighted sums of the variates and the decision as to which method of analysis to employ in any particular investigation must depend on the purpose of the investigation and the questions being asked. Most psychologists, however, agree that the factor model is best suited to their needs. It is justified on both practical and theoretical grounds. On the practical side there is the possibility of accounting adequately for the covariance structure between a relatively large set of observed variates by a smaller set of common factors. On the theoretical side there is the belief that the determinants of human behaviour, whatever their basic nature, may prove capable of description in terms of a relatively small number of mental factors or attributes, or may be shown to function *as if* they were organized in some such manner.

In situations in which a single factor ($k = 1$) is sufficient to account for the correlation between the variates, the loadings are uniquely determined. But when $k > 1$ neither the factors nor their loadings are defined uniquely, for in eqs (1.1) the factors f_r may be replaced by any orthogonal transformation of them, with a corresponding transformation of the loadings. Because of this the custom has developed of transforming or 'rotating' the factors obtained in any particular investigation so that variates of a given type—which measure, to a greater or lesser degree, some easily recognizable aspect of behaviour or performance, for instance 'verbal fluency' or 'motor speed'—may have as high loadings as possible on one factor, which is then appropriately labelled, and zero or near zero loadings on other factors in the analysis.

The lack of uniqueness combined with the fact that different experimenters have sometimes rotated factors to rather different positions, though perhaps labelling them alike, has led to a great deal of confusion about the interpretation of factors. The problems which arise will be considered in Chapters 5 and 6 where recent methods will be presented which enable the arbitrariness inherent in factor rotation to be, in large part, resolved. These methods require the experimenter to postulate in advance not only the number of factors which he expects from his analysis but also to state which variates should have zero or near zero loadings on the different factors. In pilot studies an experimenter could hardly be expected to do this, but in well planned confirmatory studies it should be possible. In the past, various empirical rules have been laid down to guide the experimenter in a search for 'meaningful' factors, of which Thurstone's concept of 'simple structure' is the best known (Thurstone, 1947), but, since it seems impossible to define this concept precisely, it will not be considered in this book.

1.4. Factor scores

When a principal component analysis is employed, scores on the components can be calculated; indeed a reciprocal relationship exists between them and the scores on the observed variates. In factor analysis, on the other hand, where the total variance of the variates is not accounted for by the common factors f_r, the problem is more difficult, for the factor scores cannot be estimated in the usual statistical sense. Some further 'Least Squares' principle has to be invoked to obtain 'estimates' for them (Chapter 7). In factor analysis estimation may therefore be regarded as a two-stage process. First the factor structure is estimated (Chapters 2, 3, 5 and 6): by this is meant the number of factors required to account for the correlation between the variates, and the loadings of the factors in these variates. When this has been done there remains the problem of estimating the scores of the individual members of the sample for the factors themselves. Two methods of doing this, one due to Thomson (1936, 1951) and the other to Bartlett (1937), are available and will be described in Chapter 7.

1.5. Comparing results from different analyses

A question which naturally arises in factor analysis is whether, for a given set of variates, the same factors occur in different populations. The difficulties of answering this question are due not only to the arbitrariness of factor rotation but also to the fact that in different populations the factors, and the variates which depend upon them, may undergo varying degrees of selection. Differences in the covariance matrices are then produced. Attempts in the past to deal with such difficulties have not proved very satisfactory and this has led us to suggest a new model for testing the permanence of factor structures. This model is described and illustrated in Chapter 8.

In this book we do not quote any formulae for the standard errors of estimated factor loadings. Those so far derived (Lawley, 1953) apply only under rather restrictive assumptions. It seems clear that some more general formulae, even if they could be derived, would be too complicated to be of much practical use.

1.6. Matrix algebra

Finally, for the benefit of readers who are not very familiar with matrix algebra, we include an Appendix which briefly reviews those definitions and results in the theory of matrices and determinants which are required for an understanding of the book.

A SELECTED LIST OF REFERENCES

Anderson, T. W. and Rubin, H. (1956), Statistical inference in factor analysis, *Proc. Third Berkeley Symposium* **5,** 111–150

Bartlett, M. S. (1937), The statistical conception of mental factors, *Brit. J. Psychol. Gen. Sect.* **28,** 97–104

Bartlett, M. S. (1938), Methods of estimating mental factors, *Nature* **141,** 609–610

Bartlett, M. S. (1950), Tests of significance in factor analysis, *Brit. J. Psychol., Statist. Sect.* **3,** 77–85

Bartlett, M. S. (1953), Factor analysis in psychology as a statistician sees it, in *Uppsala Symposium on Psychological Factor Analysis*, Nordisk Psykologi's Monograph Series No. 3, 23–34. Copenhagen: Ejnar Mundsgaards; Stockholm: Almqvist and Wiksell

Burt, C. (1940), *The Factors of the Mind*, London University Press

Burt, C. (1949), Alternative methods of factor analysis and their relations to Pearson's method of principal axes, *Brit. J. Psychol., Statist. Sect.* **2,** 98–121

Burt, C. (1950), Group factor analysis, *Brit. J. Psychol., Statist. Sect.* **3,** 40–75

Carroll, J. B. (1953), An analytical solution for approximating simple structure in factor analysis, *Psychometrika* **18,** 23–38

Creasy, M. A. (1957), Analysis of variance as an alternative to factor analysis, *J. Roy. Statist. Soc.* **19,** 318–325

Emmett, W. G. (1949), Factor analysis by Lawley's method of maximum likelihood, *Brit. J. Psychol., Statist. Sect.* **2,** 90–97

Eysenck, H. J. (1953), The logical basis of factor analysis, *The Amer. Psychologist* **8,** 105–114

Harman, H. H. (1960), *Modern Factor Analysis*, University of Chicago Press

Hotelling, H. (1933), Analysis of a complex of statistical variables into principal components, *J. Educ. Psychol.* **24,** 417–441, 498–520

Hotelling, H. (1957), The relation of the newer multivariate statistical methods to factor analysis, *Brit. J. Statist. Psychol.* **10,** 69–79

Howe, W. G. (1955), Some contributions to factor analysis, *USAEC Rep.* ORNL–1919

Jowett, G. H. (1958), Factor analysis, *Appl. Statistics* **7,** 114–125

Kaiser, H. F. (1958), The varimax criterion for analytic rotation in factor analysis, *Psychometrika* **23,** 187–200

Kendall, M. G. (1950), Factor analysis as a statistical technique, *J. Roy. Statist. Soc.* **B12,** 60–73

Kendall, M. G. (1957), *A Course in Multivariate Analysis,* London: Griffin & Co. Ltd.

Kendall, M. G. and Lawley, D. N. (1956), The principles of factor analysis, *J. Roy. Statist. Soc.* **A119,** 83–84

Lawley, D. N. (1940), The estimation of factor loadings by the method of maximum likelihood, *Proc. Roy. Soc. Edin.* **A40,** 64–82

Lawley, D. N. (1953), A modified method of estimation in factor analysis and some large sample results, *Uppsala Symposium on Psychological Factor Analysis,* Nordisk Psykologi's Monograph Series No. **3,** 35–42. Copenhagen: Ejnar Mundsgaards; Stockholm: Almqvist and Wiksell

Lawley, D. N. (1955), A statistical examination of the centroid method, *Proc. Roy. Soc. Edin.* **A64,** 175–189

Lawley, D. N. (1958), Estimation in factor analysis under various initial assumptions, *Brit. J. Statist. Psychol.* **11,** 1–12

Lawley, D. N. (1960), Approximate methods in factor analysis, *Brit. J. Statist. Psychol.* **13,** 11–17

Maxwell, A. E. (1959), Statistical methods in factor analysis, *Psychol. Bull.* **56,** 228–235

Maxwell A.E. (1961), Recent trends in factor analysis, *J. Roy. Statist. Soc.* **A124,** 49–59

Pearson, K. (1901), On lines and planes of closest fit to a system of points in space, *Phil. Mag.* **2,** 6th Series, 557–572

Rao, C. R. (1955), Estimation and tests of significance in factor analysis, *Psychometrika* **20,** 93–111

Spearman, C. (1904), General intelligence objectively determined and measured, *Amer. J. Psychol.* **15,** 201–293

Spearman, C. (1926 and 1932), *The Abilities of Man,* London: Macmillan

Thomson, G. H. (1916), A hierarchy without a general factor, *Brit. J. Psychol.* **8,** 271–281

Thomson, G. H. (1934), Hotelling's method modified to give Spearman's g, *J. Educ. Psychol.* **25,** 366–374

Thomson, G. H. (1936), Some points of mathematical technique in the factorial analysis of ability, *J. Educ. Psychol.* **27,** 37–54

Thomson, G. H. (1939 and 1951), *The Factorial Analysis of Human Ability,* London University Press

Thomson, G. H. (1954), *The Geometry of Mental Measurement,* London University Press

Thurstone, L. L. (1935), *The Vectors of the Mind*, University of Chicago Press

Thurstone, L. L. (1947), *Multiple Factor Analysis*, University of Chicago Press

Whittle, P. (1953), A principal components and least squares method of factor analysis, *Skandinavisk Aktuarietidskrift*, **35**, 223–239

Wrigley, C. and Neuhaus, J. C. (1954), The minimax method: an analytical approach to orthogonal simple structure, *Brit. J. Statist. Psychol.* **7**, 81–91

2

ESTIMATING FACTOR LOADINGS BY THE METHOD OF MAXIMUM LIKELIHOOD

2.1. Introduction

In this chapter the problem of obtaining efficient estimates of factor loadings and of residual variances is considered and a numerical example given. A large-sample test, which enables one to decide how many factors are necessary in any particular analysis, is also derived.

The discussion begins with eqs (1.1), to which the reader should refer. These equations state the basic assumption of factor analysis, namely that a set of observed correlated variates x_i $(i = 1, 2, \ldots, p)$ can be accounted for in terms of a *smaller* set of hypothetical variates or common factors f_r $(r = 1, 2, \ldots, k)$, together with a set of p independent residual variates, the main interest of the analysis being in the f_r. Note also the assumptions following eqs (1.1).

2.2. Derivation of the equations of estimation

It is assumed that the x_i follow a multivariate normal distribution. Their variances and covariances form a $p \times p$ matrix $\mathbf{C} = [c_{ij}]$. The common factors f_r are assumed to be orthogonal or uncorrelated. It follows from eqs (1.1) that the c_{ij} are given in terms of the loadings and the residual variances by

$$\begin{aligned} c_{ii} &= \sum_{r=1}^{k} l_{ir}^2 + v_i, \\ c_{ij} &= \sum_{r=1}^{k} l_{ir} l_{jr} \quad (i \neq j). \end{aligned} \tag{2.1}$$

In terms of matrix algebra these equations may be written as

$$\mathbf{C} = \mathbf{LL}' + \mathbf{V}, \tag{2.2}$$

where $\mathbf{L} = [l_{ir}]$ is the $p \times k$ matrix of loadings and $\mathbf{V}$ is the diagonal matrix with elements v_i.

The basic model thus implies a hypothesis H_0 regarding the covariance matrix $\mathbf{C}$, namely that it can be expressed as the sum of a diagonal matrix with positive elements and a matrix of rank k with positive latent roots. The value postulated for k must not be too large, otherwise this hypothesis would be trivially true. If the v_i were known we should merely require $k < p$, but in the more usual case where they are unknown the condition becomes $(p+k) < (p-k)^2$ (see Section 2.6).

Let $\mathbf{A} = [a_{ij}]$ be a sample covariance matrix whose elements are the usual sample estimates of the variances and covariances of the x_i with n degrees of freedom (corresponding as a rule to a sample of size $n+1$). Our object is to use the information provided by $\mathbf{A}$ to obtain a set of consistent and efficient estimates of the parameters l_{ir} and v_i, all supposed unknown. Since the x_i are normally distributed, the a_{ij} follow a Wishart distribution and the log-likelihood function is, omitting a function of the observations, given by

$$L = -\tfrac{1}{2}n \log_e |\mathbf{C}| - \tfrac{1}{2}n \sum_{i,j} a_{ij}c^{ij}, \tag{2.3}$$

where c^{ij} is the element in the ith row and jth column of $\mathbf{C}^{-1}$. The sum may alternatively be written as $\mathrm{tr}(\mathbf{AC}^{-1})$.

The method of maximum likelihood will be employed to estimate the unknown parameters. We shall maximize the above expression with respect to the l_{ir} and the v_i. As mentioned in Chapter 1, a difficulty arises when $k > 1$ because there are then too many l-parameters in the basic model for them to be specified uniquely. In eqs (1.1) the factors may be replaced by any orthogonal transformation of them. The effect on the loadings is that $\mathbf{L}$ is post-multiplied by a $k \times k$ orthogonal matrix. But any such post-multiplication leaves $\mathbf{LL}'$, and hence also $\mathbf{C}$, unaltered. This means that the maximum likelihood method, though it provides a unique set of estimates of the c_{ij}, leads to equations for estimating the l_{ir} which are satisfied by an infinity of solutions, all equally good from a statistical point of view. In a sense it determines the k-dimensional space in which the f_r lie, but it cannot determine their directions in that space.

In this situation all the statistician can do is to select a particular solution, one which is convenient to find, and leave the experimenter to apply whatever rotation he thinks desirable. We shall in fact choose $\mathbf{L}$ in such a way that the $k \times k$ matrix

$$\mathbf{J} = \mathbf{L}'\mathbf{V}^{-1}\mathbf{L}$$

is diagonal. We shall ignore the possibility that any of the diagonal elements of $\mathbf{J}$ are equal, which is unlikely in practice, and suppose that they are arranged in order of magnitude. This fixes **L** except that any column may have its elements reversed in sign.

In maximizing L we equate to zero its partial derivatives with respect to the l's and the v's. To obtain these we note that the partial derivative of $\log_e |\mathbf{C}|$ with respect to l_{ir} is (Appendix, eq (3))

$$2 \sum_j l_{jr} C_{ij} / |\mathbf{C}| = 2 \sum_j l_{jr} c^{ji},$$

where C_{ij} denotes the cofactor of c_{ij} in $|\mathbf{C}|$. Its partial derivative with respect to v_i is $C_{ii}/|\mathbf{C}| = c^{ii}$. The sum in (2.3) may be written as

$$\sum_{u,w} a_{uw} C_{uw} / |\mathbf{C}|.$$

The partial derivative of this with respect to l_{ir} is

$$2 \sum_{u,w,j} a_{uw} l_{jr} C_{uw,ij} / |\mathbf{C}| - \sum_{u,w} a_{uw} C_{uw} \times 2 \sum_j l_{jr} C_{ij} / |\mathbf{C}|^2,$$

where in the first summation $u \neq i$, $w \neq j$, and where $C_{uw,ij}$ denotes the cofactor of c_{ij} in C_{uw}. On using the identity

$$C_{uw,ij} |\mathbf{C}| = C_{uw} C_{ij} - C_{uj} C_{iw}$$

(Appendix, eq (4)) the above expression reduces to

$$-2 \sum_{u,w,j} a_{uw} l_{jr} C_{uj} C_{iw} / |\mathbf{C}|^2$$

$$= -2 \sum_{j,u,w} l_{jr} c^{ju} a_{uw} c^{wi}.$$

Similarly the partial derivative of the sum in (2.3) with respect to v_i is

$$- \sum_{u,w} c^{iu} a_{uw} c^{wi}.$$

Hence $\partial L / \partial l_{ir}$ is found to be $-n$ times

$$\sum_j l_{jr} c^{ji} - \sum_{j,u,w} l_{jr} c^{ju} a_{uw} c^{wi},$$

which is the element in the rth row and ith column of the matrix

$$\mathbf{L}' \mathbf{C}^{-1} - \mathbf{L}' \mathbf{C}^{-1} \mathbf{A} \mathbf{C}^{-1};$$

while $\partial L / \partial v_i$ is $-\frac{1}{2} n$ times

$$c^{ii} - \sum_{u,w} c^{iu} a_{uw} c^{wi},$$

which is the ith diagonal element of the matrix

$$\mathbf{C}^{-1}-\mathbf{C}^{-1}\mathbf{A}\mathbf{C}^{-1}.$$

The estimated loading matrix $\hat{\mathbf{L}} = [\hat{l}_{ir}]$, residual variance matrix $\hat{\mathbf{V}}$ and covariance matrix $\hat{\mathbf{C}} = [\hat{c}_{ij}]$ are therefore given by the equations

$$\hat{\mathbf{L}}'\hat{\mathbf{C}}^{-1}-\hat{\mathbf{L}}'\hat{\mathbf{C}}^{-1}\mathbf{A}\hat{\mathbf{C}}^{-1} = 0, \tag{2.4}$$

$$\operatorname{diag}(\hat{\mathbf{C}}^{-1}-\hat{\mathbf{C}}^{-1}\mathbf{A}\mathbf{C}^{-1}) = 0, \tag{2.5}$$

where diag($\mathbf{X}$) denotes the matrix consisting only of the diagonal part of $\mathbf{X}$, and

$$\hat{\mathbf{C}} = \hat{\mathbf{L}}\hat{\mathbf{L}}'+\hat{\mathbf{V}}.$$

The matrix

$$\hat{\mathbf{J}} = \hat{\mathbf{L}}'\hat{\mathbf{V}}^{-1}\hat{\mathbf{L}}$$

is restricted to being diagonal.

These equations may be considerably simplified. At this point it will be convenient to drop the circumflex accents since this can be done without ambiguity. Until otherwise stated, $\mathbf{L}$, $\mathbf{V}$ and $\mathbf{C}$ and their elements will refer to estimated values. We first post-multiply by $\mathbf{C}$ in eq (2.4) to obtain

$$\mathbf{L}'-\mathbf{L}'\mathbf{C}^{-1}\mathbf{A} = 0. \tag{2.6}$$

In (2.5) we now pre-multiply by $\mathbf{V}$, in the form $\mathbf{C}-\mathbf{L}\mathbf{L}'$, and use (2.6). This yields

$$\operatorname{diag}(\mathbf{I}-\mathbf{A}\mathbf{C}^{-1}) = 0. \tag{2.7}$$

Post-multiplication of this by $\mathbf{V}$ in the same form and further use of (2.6) thus gives

$$\operatorname{diag}(\mathbf{C}-\mathbf{A}) = 0.$$

Thus, for all i, $c_{ii} = a_{ii}$, or

$$v_i = a_{ii}-\sum_{r=1}^{k} l_{ir}^2. \tag{2.8}$$

Eq (2.6) has still to be put in a form suitable for practical solution. We make use of the identity

$$\mathbf{C}^{-1} = \mathbf{V}^{-1}-\mathbf{V}^{-1}\mathbf{L}(\mathbf{I}+\mathbf{J})^{-1}\mathbf{L}'\mathbf{V}^{-1}, \tag{2.9}$$

with $\mathbf{J}$ as before. This can be simply verified if the right-hand side is multiplied by $\mathbf{C}$ in the form $\mathbf{L}\mathbf{L}'+\mathbf{V}$. Pre-multiplication by $\mathbf{L}'$ in (2.9) gives the further identity

$$\mathbf{L}'\mathbf{C}^{-1} = (\mathbf{I}+\mathbf{J})^{-1}\mathbf{L}'\mathbf{V}^{-1}. \tag{2.10}$$

The use of this identity in (2.6) yields the equation

$$\mathbf{L}' = (\mathbf{I}+\mathbf{J})^{-1}\mathbf{L}'\mathbf{V}^{-1}\mathbf{A},$$

which can be put in the alternative form

$$\mathbf{L}' = \mathbf{J}^{-1}(\mathbf{L}'\mathbf{V}^{-1}\mathbf{A}-\mathbf{L}'),$$

or

$$\mathbf{L}' = \mathbf{J}^{-1}\mathbf{L}'\mathbf{V}^{-1}(\mathbf{A}-\mathbf{V}). \tag{2.11}$$

From eq (2.11) it follows that the matrix

$$\mathbf{H} = \mathbf{L}'\mathbf{V}^{-1}(\mathbf{A}-\mathbf{V})\mathbf{V}^{-1}\mathbf{L}$$

is equal to $\mathbf{J}^2$ and hence is diagonal.

2.3. Solution of the equations

As explained below, eqs (2.8) and (2.11) can usually be solved by iteration. The process may be regarded as a variant of the ordinary method of finding the first few latent roots and vectors of a matrix. Inspection of eq (2.11) shows that the elements of $\mathbf{J}$, or the square roots of the elements of $\mathbf{H}$, are latent roots of $\mathbf{V}^{-1}(\mathbf{A}-\mathbf{V})$; we find the first k in order of magnitude. The rows of $\mathbf{L}'$ are the corresponding latent row vectors. We denote the rth row of $\mathbf{L}'$ by $\mathbf{l}'_r$.

To illustrate a complete cycle of the iteration procedure let us suppose that $\mathbf{L}_{(1)}$ and $\mathbf{V}_{(1)}$ are approximations to $\mathbf{L}$ and $\mathbf{V}$. Denote the rth row of $\mathbf{L}'_{(1)}$ by $\mathbf{l}'_{r(1)}$. We begin by finding the row vectors

$$\mathbf{w}'_1 = \mathbf{l}'_{1(1)}\mathbf{V}_{(1)}^{-1}$$

and

$$\mathbf{u}'_1 = \mathbf{w}'_1\mathbf{A}-\mathbf{l}'_{1(1)}$$

and the (positive) scalar $h_1 = \mathbf{u}'_1\mathbf{w}_1$. A better approximation to $\mathbf{l}'_1$ is then given by

$$\mathbf{l}'_{1(2)} = (1/\sqrt{h_1})\mathbf{u}'_1.$$

If there is a second common factor, i.e. $k \geqslant 2$, we find successively the row vector

$$\mathbf{w}'_2 = \mathbf{l}'_{2(1)}\mathbf{V}_{(1)}^{-1},$$

the scalar

$$j_{21} = \mathbf{w}'_2\mathbf{l}_{1(2)},$$

the row vector

$$\mathbf{u}'_2 = \mathbf{w}'_2\mathbf{A}-\mathbf{l}'_{2(1)}-j_{21}\mathbf{l}'_{1(2)}$$

and the scalar $h_2 = \mathbf{u}'_2\mathbf{w}_2$. A better approximation to $\mathbf{l}'_2$ is then given by

$$\mathbf{l}'_{2(2)} = (1/\sqrt{h_2})\mathbf{u}'_2.$$

For a third factor we find successively the row vector

$$\mathbf{w}'_3 = \mathbf{l}'_{3(1)}\mathbf{V}_{(1)}^{-1},$$

the two scalars

$$j_{31} = \mathbf{w}'_3\mathbf{l}_{1(2)}$$

and

$$j_{32} = \mathbf{w}'_3\mathbf{l}_{2(2)},$$

the row vector

$$\mathbf{u}'_3 = \mathbf{w}'_3\mathbf{A} - \mathbf{l}'_{3(1)} - j_{31}\mathbf{l}'_{1(2)} - j_{32}\mathbf{l}'_{2(2)}$$

and the scalar $h_3 = \mathbf{u}'_3\mathbf{w}_3$. A better approximation to $\mathbf{l}'_3$ is then given by

$$\mathbf{l}'_{3(2)} = (1/\sqrt{h_3})\mathbf{u}'_3.$$

We proceed similarly for any value of k. Better estimates of the v_i, forming a matrix $\mathbf{V}_{(2)}$, are found by use of eqs (2.8). The new matrices of estimates, $\mathbf{L}_{(2)}$ and $\mathbf{V}_{(2)}$, may be used to initiate a new cycle of iteration. It has not been found possible to establish exact conditions under which the above procedure converges, but in practice this is usually the case. Convergence is, however, often very slow and, as Howe (1955) has pointed out, it is possible for differences between successive iterates to be extremely small and yet to be far from the exact solution. In most cases this probably does not matter very much since later iterations make little alteration to the estimated covariances and hence do not materially improve the fit. There is thus not much to be gained by obtaining an exact solution.

It is possible to construct $\mathbf{A}$-matrices for which the maximum likelihood method breaks down, either because there is no solution in terms of real numbers or because one or more of the v_i are zero. Breakdowns of this nature have been known to occur in other fields of research, but are fortunately rare in practice.

Except by accident, or in trivial cases, the non-diagonal elements of $\mathbf{C}$ (or $\hat{\mathbf{C}}$) are not equal to the corresponding elements of $\mathbf{A}$. The best estimate of the covariance between x_i

and x_j under the hypothesis H_0 is given by $\hat{c}_{ij}$, and not by a_{ij}.

A satisfactory property of the above method of estimation is that it is independent of the metric used. A change of scale of any variate x_i merely induces proportional changes in its loadings l_{ir}. This may easily be verified by examination of the equations of estimation.

2.4. A numerical example

To illustrate the calculations in a maximum likelihood analysis, data reported by Emmett (1949) for nine variates and a sample of 211 subjects are used. The matrix of correlations is given in Table 2.1; it may be regarded as a standardized covariance matrix. Below it are given details of the calculations. In the first instance the hypothesis that two factors are adequate to explain the correlations is considered. One cycle of the iterations only is shown. Since Emmett's analysis was published, a programme for obtaining maximum likelihood estimates of loadings on the Mercury Electronic Computer has been written (Nixon and Maxwell, 1960), and the results have been reported.

Emmett began his iterations with estimates of the loadings given by a centroid analysis (see Chapter 3). This is generally a wise procedure since good initial estimates greatly facilitate the iterative procedure. However, it was possible—with a computer available—to try rough guesses at the loadings, as well as centroid estimates, for starting values, and in this instance convergence was reached without difficulty. In general such is not the case and it is recommended that the best available estimates should be employed at the outset, otherwise convergence may not be attained or may be a very slow process.

The rows in Table 2.1 showing the details of the calculations are labelled with the appropriate symbols. The first two rows give the centroid loadings which are employed as initial estimates. In the third row the initial estimates of the residual variances appear ($\mathbf{V}_{(1)}$ is, of course, really diagonal). They are obtained by subtracting the sum of the squares of the loadings of each variate on the two factors from unity. For instance the first entry in the third row is $1-(0{\cdot}718^2+0{\cdot}231^2) = 0{\cdot}431$. The elements in rows $\mathbf{w}'_1$ and $\mathbf{w}'_2$ are obtained respectively by dividing the elements in the first two rows by the corresponding elements in the third row. The row labelled $\mathbf{u}'_1$, given by the expression $\mathbf{u}'_1 = \mathbf{w}'_1\mathbf{A} - \mathbf{l}'_{1(1)}$,

Table 2.1. Correlation matrix and details of calculations

	1	*2*	*3*	*4*	*5*	*6*	*7*	*8*	*9*	Check column
	1·000	0·523	0·395	0·471	0·346	0·426	0·576	0·434	0·639	4·810
	0·523	1·000	0·479	0·506	0·418	0·462	0·547	0·283	0·645	4·863
	0·395	0·479	1·000	0·355	0·270	0·254	0·452	0·219	0·504	3·928
	0·471	0·506	0·355	1·000	0·691	0·791	0·443	0·285	0·505	5·047
	0·346	0·418	0·270	0·691	1·000	0·679	0·383	0·149	0·409	4·345
	0·426	0·462	0·254	0·791	0·679	1·000	0·372	0·314	0·472	4·770
	0·576	0·547	0·452	0·443	0·383	0·372	1·000	0·385	0·680	4·838
	0·434	0·283	0·219	0·285	0·149	0·314	0·385	1·000	0·470	3·539
	0·639	0·645	0·504	0·505	0·409	0·472	0·680	0·470	1·000	5·324
$\mathbf{l}'_{1(1)}$	0·718	0·728	0·554	0·781	0·652	0·736	0·729	0·486	0·808	6·192
$\mathbf{l}'_{2(1)}$	0·231	0·127	0·221	−0·436	−0·450	−0·474	0·288	0·200	0·305	0·012
$\mathbf{V}_{(1)}$	0·431	0·454	0·644	0·200	0·372	0·234	0·386	0·724	0·254	
$\mathbf{w}'_1$	1·666	1·604	0·860	3·905	1·753	3·145	1·889	0·671	3·181	
$\mathbf{u}'_1$	9·324	9·596	6·995	11·359	9·538	10·772	9·378	6·134	10·679	83·775
$\mathbf{l}'_{1(2)}$	0·681	0·700	0·511	0·829	0·696	0·786	0·685	0·448	0·779	6·115
$\mathbf{w}'_2$	0·536	0·280	0·343	−2·180	−1·210	−2·026	0·746	0·276	1·201	
$\mathbf{u}'_2$	0·913	0·668	0·844	−1·047	−1·082	−1·201	1·141	0·744	1·184	2·164
$\mathbf{l}'_{2(2)}$	0·297	0·217	0·274	−0·340	−0·352	−0·390	0·371	0·242	0·385	0·704

$h_1 = 187{\cdot}697$ $1/\sqrt{h_1} = 0{\cdot}07299$ $j_{21} = -1{\cdot}935$ $h_2 = 9{\cdot}469$ $1/\sqrt{h_2} = 0{\cdot}3250$

can be calculated directly when a desk machine is being used. The first element in it, for example, is the inner product of $\mathbf{w}'_1$ with the first column (or row) of the correlation matrix reduced by 0·718 (the first element in $\mathbf{l}'_{1(1)}$). Similarly, after j_{21} has been found, row $\mathbf{u}'_2$ can be calculated directly on a desk machine in the form $\mathbf{u}'_2 = \mathbf{w}'_2\mathbf{A} - \mathbf{l}'_{2(1)} - j'_{21}\mathbf{l}'_{1(2)}$. The elements of $\mathbf{l}'_{1(2)}$ are those of $\mathbf{u}'_1$ multiplied by $1/\sqrt{h_1}$, that is 0·07299; while the elements of $\mathbf{l}'_{2(2)}$ are those of $\mathbf{u}'_2$ multiplied by $1/\sqrt{h_2}$, that is 0·3250.

When the calculations are done on a desk machine a check column is also useful. For instance the inner product of $\mathbf{w}'_1$ and the vector of row totals of $\mathbf{A}$ is 89·968. When the sum of row $\mathbf{l}'_{1(1)}$, namely 6·192, is subtracted from this value we get 83·776, which is (ignoring rounding-off errors) the sum of row $\mathbf{u}'_1$. Similarly the inner product of $\mathbf{w}'_2$ and the row totals

Table 2.2. Maximum likelihood estimates of the loadings for two factors, I and II

	Variates				
	1	*2*	*3*	*4*	*5*
I	0·668	0·692	0·500	0·839	0·700
II	0·304	0·236	0·287	−0·321	−0·319

	Variates			
	6	*7*	*8*	*9*
I	0·800	0·670	0·442	0·775
II	−0·372	0·385	0·245	0·424

of $\mathbf{A}$ is −9·657, and on subtracting from it the sum of row $\mathbf{l}'_{2(1)}$, namely 0·012, and the product of j_{21} and the sum of row $\mathbf{l}'_{1(2)}$, which is −11·833, we get 2·164, which is the sum of row $\mathbf{u}'_2$.

A second cycle of the iterative process can now be performed employing the new estimates of the loadings given in rows $\mathbf{l}'_{1(2)}$ and $\mathbf{l}'_{2(2)}$ of Table 2.1, and the procedure can be continued until the loadings converge to stationary values. The final values, obtained after a large number of iterations on the computer, are given in Table 2.2. The total variance is 9 and the percentage extracted by each of the factors can be obtained by finding

$$(100/9) \sum_i l_{ir}^2$$

for $r = 1, 2$. The values are 47·3 and 10·7 per cent.

The next stage in the process is to find the residual covariance matrix $\mathbf{A}-\mathbf{LL}'$, where $\mathbf{L}'$ is the matrix of loadings given in Table 2.2, and to test whether the hypothesis that there are two factors is confirmed. The details of this will be given later.

Prior evidence suggested that a third factor, having an appreciable loading in variate *8* at least, might exist. To investigate this possibility centroid loadings for a third factor were calculated. These are as follows:

Variates				
1	*2*	*3*	*4*	*5*
−0·131	0·170	0·239	0·047	0·179

Variates			
6	*7*	*8*	*9*
−0·134	0·066	−0·350	−0·043

Using them in conjunction with the estimates for the two factors already obtained, maximum likelihood estimates of the loadings for three factors were found. Those given by the Mercury computer are shown in Table 2.3 where, as anticipated, the highest loading for the third factor is in variate *8*.

Table 2.3. Maximum likelihood loadings for three factors, I, II and III

	Variates				
	1	*2*	*3*	*4*	*5*
I	0·664	0·688	0·492	0·837	0·705
II	0·322	0·248	0·304	−0·291	−0·314
III	−0·075	0·192	0·224	0·037	0·155

	Variates			
	6	*7*	*8*	*9*
I	0·820	0·661	0·457	0·765
II	−0·377	0·397	0·294	0·428
III	−0·104	0·077	−0·488	0·009

As an experiment it was now decided to repeat the analysis employing less accurate initial approximations to the loadings than those given by a centroid analysis. Those used were as follows:

Factors	*Variates*								
	1	*2*	*3*	*4*	*5*	*6*	*7*	*8*	*9*
I	0·6	0·6	0·6	0·6	0·6	0·6	0·6	0·6	0·6
II	0·3	0·3	0·3	−0·3	−0·3	−0·3	0·3	0·3	0·3
III	0·0	0·2	0·2	0·0	0·0	0·0	0·0	−0·4	0·0

They led, without complication or loss of computer time, to the values previously found (Table 2.3).

This appears to be an exceptional case. Experience has shown that in the absence of good initial approximations to the loadings, some difficulties can arise. A common occurrence, when three or more factors are postulated at the outset, is for one of the loadings to approach unity and then the method breaks down. To combat this Lord (1958) has suggested that when convergence for a small number of factors has been obtained, approximate estimates (see Chapter 3) of the loadings for the next factor should be obtained from the residuals. These can then be included in the iterative process, and this procedure can be repeated for each succeeding factor.

2.5. Improvement of initial estimates

It is also worth noting that if $\mathbf{L}$ is *any* matrix of approximate loadings, convergence may be hastened by starting with $\mathbf{L}_{(1)} = \mathbf{LU}$, rather than $\mathbf{L}$, where $\mathbf{U}$ is a $k \times k$ orthogonal matrix chosen so that the matrix

$$\mathbf{U}'(\mathbf{L}'\mathbf{V}^{-1}\mathbf{L})\mathbf{U} = \mathbf{L}'_{(1)}\mathbf{V}^{-1}\mathbf{L}_{(1)}$$

is diagonal (see Appendix). To illustrate the procedure the first two rows below the correlation matrix in Table 2.1 may be taken as $\mathbf{L}'$, and the third row as $\mathbf{V}$ (which is diagonal). Using these values we find

$$\mathbf{L}'\mathbf{V}^{-1}\mathbf{L} = \begin{bmatrix} 13{\cdot}622 & -1{\cdot}556 \\ -1{\cdot}556 & 3{\cdot}327 \end{bmatrix}.$$

The first latent row vector of this matrix is $[1{\cdot}000 \; -0{\cdot}148]$ and when its elements are normalized, so that the sum of their squares is unity, we obtain $[0{\cdot}989 \; -0{\cdot}146]$. The rotation matrix $\mathbf{U}'$, which is of the form

$$\begin{bmatrix} \cos\theta & -\sin\theta \\ \sin\theta & \cos\theta \end{bmatrix},$$

is therefore

$$\begin{bmatrix} 0{\cdot}989 & -0{\cdot}146 \\ 0{\cdot}146 & 0{\cdot}989 \end{bmatrix}.$$

The adjusted initial trial estimates of the factor loadings are given by $\mathbf{L}'_{(1)} = \mathbf{U}'\mathbf{L}'$ and are

0·676	0·701	0·516	0·836	0·711	0·797	0·679	0·451	0·755
0·333	0·232	0·299	−0·317	−0·350	−0·361	0·391	0·269	0·420

After one cycle of the iterative process using these estimates we obtain $\mathbf{L}'_{(2)}$, whose elements are

0·671	0·693	0·501	0·839	0·707	0·798	0·672	0·440	0·767
0·318	0·239	0·290	−0·313	−0·329	−0·365	0·392	0·256	0·410

The latter values are noticeably closer in numerical value (when the slowness of the convergence process is borne in mind) to the final values given in Table 2.2 than are the values in rows $\mathbf{l}'_{1(2)}$ and $\mathbf{l}'_{2(2)}$ of Table 2.1. Hence it is seen that, even in this small and rather straightforward example, the advantage of choosing $\mathbf{L}'$ such that $\mathbf{L}'_{(1)}\mathbf{V}^{-1}\mathbf{L}_{(1)}$ is diagonal is considerable.

2.6. Testing hypotheses about the number of factors

We shall now discuss the problem of testing the hypothesis H_0 that there are precisely k common factors. A satisfactory test is possible only if n is moderately large, in which case we can construct a criterion of the large-sample χ^2 type, found by the likelihood ratio method of Neyman and Pearson. At this point we shall revert to the use of circumflex accents to denote estimates. The symbols **L**, **V** and **C**, used without accents, will refer to true values.

If H_0 is true, then $\hat{\mathbf{C}}$ provides the best etsimates of the variances and covariances. Substitution of $\hat{\mathbf{C}}$ for **C** in the expression (2.3) for the log-likelihood gives

$$L_0 = -\tfrac{1}{2}n \log_e |\hat{\mathbf{C}}| - \tfrac{1}{2}n \operatorname{tr}(\mathbf{A}\hat{\mathbf{C}}^{-1}).$$

If, on the other hand, we merely assume the normality of the x_i but make no further hypothesis about **C**, then **A** provides the best estimate for **C**. Substitution of **A** for **C** in (2.3) gives

$$\begin{aligned} L_1 &= -\tfrac{1}{2}n \log_e |\mathbf{A}| - \tfrac{1}{2}n \operatorname{tr}(\mathbf{A}\mathbf{A}^{-1}) \\ &= -\tfrac{1}{2}n (\log_e |\mathbf{A}| + p). \end{aligned}$$

It is well known that for large samples $2(L_1 - L_0)$ is distributed approximately as χ^2. This gives as a criterion the expression

$$n\{\log_e (|\hat{\mathbf{C}}|/|\mathbf{A}|) + \operatorname{tr}(\mathbf{A}\hat{\mathbf{C}}^{-1}) - p\}. \tag{2.12}$$

The number of degrees of freedom for χ^2 is equal to the number, $\tfrac{1}{2}p(p+1)$, of variances and covariances minus the effective number of unknown parameters which, under H_0, have to be estimated. On account of the indeterminacy arising from possible rotations of the factors, the effective number of unknown parameters is

$$p+pk-\tfrac{1}{2}k(k-1)$$
$$= p+\tfrac{1}{2}k+\tfrac{1}{2}p^2-\tfrac{1}{2}(p-k)^2.$$

Hence the number of degrees of freedom for χ^2 is

$$\tfrac{1}{2}\{(p-k)^2-(p+k)\}. \qquad (2.13)$$

This is positive provided that H_0 is non-trivial.

It has been pointed out by Bartlett (1951) that the distribution of the criterion (2.12) approximates more closely to that of χ^2 if n is replaced by the multiplying factor

$$n' = n-\tfrac{1}{6}(2p+5)-\tfrac{2}{3}k. \qquad (2.14)$$

(Strictly speaking this is slightly conjectural. The multiplying factor in the special case where $k = 0$ is known to be $n-\frac{1}{6}(2p+5)$. For $k > 0$ it seems reasonable to replace n by $n-k$ and p by $p-k$.)

If the equations of estimation have been solved *exactly*, then by (2.7) we have $\mathrm{tr}(\mathbf{A}\hat{\mathbf{C}}^{-1}) = \mathrm{tr}(\mathbf{I}_p) = p$. Hence expression (2.12) may be replaced by

$$n' \log_e (|\hat{\mathbf{C}}|/|\mathbf{A}|). \qquad (2.15)$$

On the other hand, if insufficient iterations have been performed to obtain an exact solution, use of (2.15) may well give an entirely false result. In fact a negative value for χ^2 may even be obtained!

The calculation of either (2.12) or (2.15) is to some extent simplified if we note that

$$\begin{aligned} |\hat{\mathbf{C}}| &= |\hat{\mathbf{V}}+\hat{\mathbf{L}}\hat{\mathbf{L}}'| \\ &= |\hat{\mathbf{V}}(\mathbf{I}_p+\hat{\mathbf{V}}^{-1}\hat{\mathbf{L}}\hat{\mathbf{L}}')| \\ &= |\hat{\mathbf{V}}|\times|\mathbf{I}_p+\hat{\mathbf{V}}^{-1}\hat{\mathbf{L}}\hat{\mathbf{L}}'| \\ &= |\hat{\mathbf{V}}|\times|\mathbf{I}_k+\hat{\mathbf{L}}'\hat{\mathbf{V}}^{-1}\hat{\mathbf{L}}| \text{ (Appendix, result 7).} \end{aligned} \qquad (2.16)$$

The first factor in the last line is merely $\hat{v}_1\hat{v}_2 \ldots \hat{v}_p$, while the second is a determinant of order k. By the use of identity (2.9) it is also easy to show that

$$\mathrm{tr}(\mathbf{A}\hat{\mathbf{C}}^{-1})-p = \mathrm{tr}\{(\mathbf{I}+\hat{\mathbf{J}})^{-1}(\hat{\mathbf{J}}^2-\hat{\mathbf{H}})\},$$

where

$$\hat{\mathbf{J}} = \hat{\mathbf{L}}'\hat{\mathbf{V}}^{-1}\hat{\mathbf{L}}$$
$$\hat{\mathbf{H}} = \hat{\mathbf{L}}'\hat{\mathbf{V}}^{-1}(\mathbf{A}-\hat{\mathbf{V}})\hat{\mathbf{V}}^{-1}\hat{\mathbf{L}}.$$

(In the case of an exact solution $\hat{\mathbf{J}}^2 = \hat{\mathbf{H}}$.)

Even with these simplifications and with moderate values of p the evaluation of either (2.12) or (2.15) is laborious since the determinant of $\mathbf{A}$ is required. Fortunately an approximation can be found which is adequate in most practical cases. This depends on the fact that, for large n, the values of the differences $a_{ij}-\hat{c}_{ij}$ tend to be small, so that terms of degree higher than the second in these differences may be neglected.

Let us suppose that the equations of estimation have been exactly satisfied and let us write the criterion of (2.15) in the form

$$-n' \log_e |\hat{\mathbf{C}}^{-1}\mathbf{A}|.$$

By the use of (2.6) and (2.9) we have

$$\begin{aligned}\hat{\mathbf{C}}^{-1}\mathbf{A} &= \mathbf{I}+\hat{\mathbf{C}}^{-1}(\mathbf{A}-\hat{\mathbf{C}}) \\ &= \mathbf{I}+\hat{\mathbf{V}}^{-1}(\mathbf{A}-)\hat{\mathbf{C}}.\end{aligned}$$

Hence the criterion may be written as

$$-n' \log_e |\mathbf{I}+\mathbf{X}|,$$

where $$\mathbf{X} = [x_{ij}] = \hat{\mathbf{V}}^{-1}(\mathbf{A}-\hat{\mathbf{C}}).$$

We now expand $|\mathbf{I}+\mathbf{X}|$, remembering that the diagonal elements of $\mathbf{X}$ are zero, and retain only the second degree terms in the x_{ij}. This gives, as approximate χ^2 criterion,

$$\begin{aligned}& n'\sum_{i<j} x_{ij}x_{ji} \\ &= n'\sum_{i<j} (a_{ij}-\hat{c}_{ij})^2/(\hat{v}_i\hat{v}_j).\end{aligned} \tag{2.17}$$

This expression is very easy to calculate. It has been found as a rule to provide a good approximation even when comparatively few iterations have been performed and when the exact maximum likelihood estimates have not been attained. We have kept n' as the multiplying factor, rather than n, although the justification for this is not very strong.

If the value of χ^2 is found to exceed the chosen level of significance, and H_0 is rejected, the conclusion is that in the basic model at least $k+1$ common factors are required.

2.7. A numerical example

To illustrate the test of significance of the residuals the residual matrix (after the effects of the first two factors given in Table 2.2 have been eliminated from the original correlation matrix, Table 2.1) is first obtained. It is given by $\mathbf{A}-\hat{\mathbf{L}}\hat{\mathbf{L}}'$, and appears in Table 2.4.

Table 2.4. Residual covariance matrix after eliminating two factors

1	*2*	*3*	*4*	*5*	*6*	*7*	*8*	*9*
0·461	−0·011	−0·026	0·007	−0·026	0·005	0·012	0·064	−0·008
−0·011	0·465	0·065	0·001	0·008	−0·004	−0·008	−0·081	0·007
−0·026	0·065	0·667	0·027	0·011	−0·040	0·007	−0·073	−0·006
0·007	0·001	0·027	0·192	0·000	0·000	0·004	−0·007	−0·010
−0·026	0·008	0·011	0·000	0·408	0·000	0·036	−0·083	0·001
0·005	−0·004	−0·040	0·000	0·000	0·221	−0·021	0·051	0·010
0·012	−0·008	0·007	0·004	0·036	−0·021	0·403	−0·006	−0·003
0·064	−0·081	−0·073	−0·007	−0·083	0·051	−0·006	0·745	0·023
−0·008	0·007	−0·006	−0·010	0·001	0·010	−0·003	0·023	0·219

Table 2.5. Residual covariance matrix after eliminating three factors

1	*2*	*3*	*4*	*5*	*6*	*7*	*8*	*9*
0·450	0·001	−0·013	0·011	−0·010	−0·004	0·015	−0·001	−0·006
0·001	0·427	0·022	−0·005	−0·019	0·011	−0·022	−0·011	0·010
−0·013	0·022	0·615	0·023	−0·016	−0·012	−0·011	0·014	−0·005
0·011	−0·005	0·023	0·214	0·003	−0·001	0·002	0·006	−0·012
−0·010	−0·019	−0·016	0·003	0·380	−0·001	0·029	−0·006	0·002
−0·004	0·011	−0·012	−0·001	−0·001	0·175	−0·012	−0·001	0·007
0·015	−0·022	−0·011	0·002	0·029	−0·012	0·399	0·003	0·003
−0·001	−0·011	0·014	0·006	−0·006	−0·001	0·003	0·466	−0·001
−0·006	0·010	−0·005	−0·012	0·002	0·007	0·003	−0·001	0·231

The diagonal values are the estimates $\hat{v}_i$ of the residual variances. The non-diagonal elements are the differences $(a_{ij}-\hat{c}_{ij})$. Probably the easiest way of evaluating (2.17) is to calculate first $\hat{\mathbf{V}}^{-1}$, then

$$\mathbf{X} = [x_{ij}] = \hat{\mathbf{V}}^{-1}(\mathbf{A}-\hat{\mathbf{C}}),$$

and hence

$$\sum_{i<j} x_{ij}x_{ji},$$

noting that $x_{ij} \neq x_{ji}$. The latter expression is then multiplied by n' as given by (2.14).

For the data in Table 2.4 we find the value of $\Sigma x_{ij}x_{ji}$ to be 0·1419. Since $n = 210$, $p = 9$, $k = 2$, we have $n' = 204{\cdot}8$, so that the value of χ^2 is 29·1. The number of degrees of freedom, found from (2.13), is 19 and reference to tables of χ^2 shows that the value falls just below the 5 per cent level of significance.

Despite this it was decided to fit a third factor, since some of the residuals, particularly those in column *8*, were rather large. Using the loadings given in Table 2.3, the residual matrix was found after eliminating three factors (Table 2.5), and the test of significance was applied again. In this case

$$\sum_{i<j} x_{ij}x_{ji}$$

was found to be 0·0352. Since $k = 3$ we now have $n' = 204{\cdot}2$, and the value of χ^2 is 7·2. This value is based on 12 degrees of freedom and is well below its expectation. There is therefore no justification for fitting more than three factors.

REFERENCES

Bartlett, M. S. (1951), The effect of standardization on an approximation in factor analysis, *Biometrika* **38**, 337–344

Emmett, W. G. (1949), Factor analysis by Lawley's method of maximum likelihood, *Brit. J. Psychol., Statist. Sect.* **2**, 90–97

Howe, W. G. (1955), Some contributions to factor analysis, *U.S.A.E.C. Rep.* ORNL–1919

Lord, F. M. (1956), A study of speed factors in tests of academic grades, *Psychometrika* **21**, 31–50

Nixon, W. L. B. and Maxwell, A. E. (1960), Programme for the maximum likelihood method of factor analysis, *Laboratory Notes*, University of London Computer Unit

3

THE CENTROID METHOD

3.1. Introduction

Although the maximum likelihood method of factor analysis is the only method available which provides efficient estimates of the factor loadings, it has not been widely adopted, largely because of the onerous calculations involved. But numerous quick approximate methods of estimating loadings are in current use. The most popular of these is the *centroid* or *simple summation method*, which is well described by numerous writers (cf. Burt, 1940; Thurstone, 1947; Thomson, 1951; Jowett, 1958). Since it provides estimates of the factor loadings which generally correspond fairly closely with maximum likelihood estimates and are adequate for most practical purposes, it deserves mention. Owing to a certain arbitrariness in its procedure, which will be shown presently, a statistical assessment of the method and an examination of its sampling properties is extremely difficult, if not impossible, and will not be attempted here. However, from what is known, the method appears to have high efficiency (Lawley, 1955), and when illustrated by means of a geometrical model (Thomson, 1954) it is easy to grasp.

3.2. Geometrical model for the centroid method

Let the variates, x_1, x_2, ..., x_p, be represented by vectors radiating from an origin in a space of p dimensions, the cosines of the angles between pairs of them being equal to the corresponding correlations. Let the lengths of the vectors, measured from the origin, be taken equal to the standard deviations of the variates they represent. Now if the directions in which the variates are scored are chosen, by temporarily reversing their signs if necessary, so that as many as possible of the correlations are positive, then the vectors will tend to cluster in a sheaf or pencil. Under these conditions the first centroid of the system is defined as the resultant of the vectors, and will pass somewhere through the middle of the sheaf.

The effect of this centroid can now be removed and, by a further reflection of signs, a new sheaf of vectors formed. A second centroid can then be removed, and so on, until the variance of the variates is completely accounted for. In general we shall have p vectors in a space of p dimensions; but the essential features of the model can be demonstrated by considering just the two-dimensional case.

Suppose that there are two variates x_1 and x_2, with variances s_1^2 and s_2^2 and correlation coefficient r. Then their covariance matrix is

$$\mathbf{A} = \begin{bmatrix} s_1^2 & rs_1s_2 \\ rs_1s_2 & s_2^2 \end{bmatrix}.$$

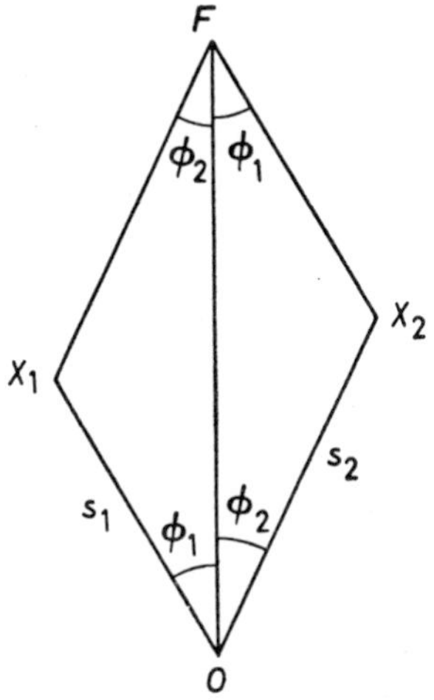

FIG. 3.1

Represent the variates x_1, x_2 by the vectors OX_1, OX_2 (Figure 3.1) at an angle θ, where

$$OX_1 = s_1, \quad OX_2 = s_2, \quad \cos\theta = r.$$

Then the resultant of OX_1 and OX_2 is represented by the vector OF, where OX_1FX_2 is a parallelogram. This vector, after standardization to unit length, represents the first centroid, or factor, f.

Let ϕ_1 and ϕ_2 be the angles which OX_1 and OX_2 make with

OF, so that $\phi_1+\phi_2 = \theta$. The loadings of x_1 and x_2 on f are given by

$$\begin{aligned} l_{1f} &= s_1 \cos\phi_1, \\ l_{2f} &= s_2 \cos\phi_2. \end{aligned} \tag{3.1}$$

If the column vector of loadings is denoted by $\mathbf{l}$, then the residual covariance matrix after removing the effect of the first centroid is

$$\mathbf{A}-\mathbf{ll}',$$

that is

$$\begin{bmatrix} s_1^2-(s_1\cos\phi_1)^2 & rs_1s_2-s_1s_2\cos\phi_1\cos\phi_2 \\ rs_1s_2-s_1s_2\cos\phi_1\cos\phi_2 & s_2^2-(s_2\cos\phi_2)^2 \end{bmatrix}$$

$$= \begin{bmatrix} s_1^2\sin^2\phi_1 & -s_1s_2\sin\phi_1\sin\phi_2 \\ -s_1s_2\sin\phi_1\sin\phi_2 & s_2^2\sin^2\phi_2 \end{bmatrix},$$

since $r = \cos(\phi_1+\phi_2)$

$$= \cos\phi_1\cos\phi_2 - \sin\phi_1\sin\phi_2.$$

As $s_1\sin\phi_1 = s_2\sin\phi_2$, the column and row totals of the above matrix vanish.

By expressing $\cos\phi_1$ and $\cos\phi_2$ in eqs (3.1) in terms of s_1, s_2 and r a simple method of calculating the loadings of the variates on the factor, direct from the covariance matrix $\mathbf{A}$, is obtained. For instance

$$\begin{aligned} l_{1f} &= s_1\cos\phi_1 \\ &= \frac{s_1(s_1+rs_2)}{\sqrt{(s_1^2+s_2^2+2rs_1s_2)}}. \end{aligned} \tag{3.2}$$

The numerator in the latter expression is the sum of the elements in the first column of $\mathbf{A}$, while the denominator is the square root of the sum of all the elements of $\mathbf{A}$. A similar expression can be obtained for l_{2f}.

Next it is necessary to obtain the loadings of the variates on the second centroid. These cannot be obtained directly from the residual matrix since its column and row sums vanish. To proceed further the sign of one or other of the variates must be reversed. This is equivalent to reversing the signs in one row and one column of the residual matrix. When this has been done the loadings of the variates on the second centroid are obtained by summing the columns and by dividing each by the square root of the sum of all the entries in the residual covariance matrix. Finally the loading of the variate which had its sign reflected must have its original sign restored.

In the case of two variates, only two centroids can be obtained, but an example in which the loadings on three centroids are found is given at the end of the chapter.

The arbitrariness in the centroid procedure, which was mentioned earlier, lies in the reversal of signs necessary to break the equilibrium which results after each centroid is extracted, and which arises from the fact that the sums of the columns in each residual matrix are zero. When the number of variates is large the reversals can be done in many different ways. A procedure often adopted is to count the number of negative signs in each column of the residual matrix, and in the matrix as a whole. The variate having the greatest number of negative signs now has its sign reversed by changing all the signs in its row and column. It is well to note that in this process the diagonal signs remain positive. The total number of negative signs in the matrix is again obtained, and the process is continued until this number is a minimum. When this is done it is to be expected that succeeding centroids will extract most of the remaining variance of the variates, although the mere counting of signs cannot ensure this, since the actual sizes of the residuals have not been taken into consideration. In cases where the original covariances are not all positive, sign reflection may be advisable before the first centroid loadings are estimated. This is so in the second example at the end of the chapter.

A disadvantage of the centroid method is that it is not independent of the metric used. The loadings obtained depend upon the scales in which the variates are measured. The usual practice is to standardize the variates, so that the covariance matrix **A** becomes the correlation matrix. This, however, leads to difficulties when tests of significance are considered.

3.3. Centroid method with 'communalities'

A complication which arises when the centroid method is used to estimate the loadings in eqs (1.1) is that the diagonal elements of **A**, i.e. the total variances, are replaced by smaller quantities known as 'communalities'. A communality represents the portion of the variance of a variate which is due to the k common factors. In other words it is the total variance minus the residual variance. As a result of this replacement the covariance matrix is reduced to a matrix of rank k, apart from sampling errors. Since the communalities (and generally the value of k) are initially unknown they are estimated by trial values; these lead to sets of loadings from which new estimates are obtained, and the final solution is arrived at by an iterative process. Convergence is, however, relatively fast. An example will help to make the arithmetical process clear.

3.4. Example of the centroid method using communalities

In Table 3.1 the correlations are given between the scores of a sample of 220 boys on the six school subjects: 1, Gaelic; 2, English; 3, History; 4, Arithmetic; 5, Algebra; 6, Geometry.

For the analysis to begin, 'guesses' at the communalities have to be made. A common procedure for a correlation matrix is to use the highest correlation coefficient in each column, which is substituted for unity in the diagonal cell. This has been done in Table 3.1. (With covariance matrices the highest correlation coefficient in the column multiplied by the variance could be used in the diagonal cell.) The columns of the matrix are now summed and the grand total, 13·212, is found. The square root of the latter is 3·635 and when each column sum is divided by this quantity the first estimates of the loadings of the variates on the first centroid are obtained. The column sums and the loadings are given in the table, below the correlation matrix. A check on the calculations is that the algebraic sum of the loadings should equal (nearly) the divisor 3·635.

The effect of the first centroid has now to be eliminated from the original matrix to get the first residual covariance matrix. If the row of loadings just obtained is denoted by the vector $\mathbf{l}'$, and the matrix with guessed communalities by $\mathbf{A}_0$, then the residual matrix is $\mathbf{A}_0 - \mathbf{l}\mathbf{l}'$. It appears in Table 3.2.

Apart from rounding-off errors the sums of the columns of this table are zero, as we should expect. Before the analysis can proceed the signs of at least one of the variates must be reversed, and our aim should be to reduce the number of negative signs to a minimum. Indeed we can make the number zero by reversing the signs of variates *4*, *5* and *6*. Next the entries for the diagonal cells of the matrix have to be considered. Since those in the table are all positive they could be used, or they

Table 3.1. Matrix of correlations of six variates with guessed communalities entered in the diagonal cells

1. Gaelic	(0·439)	0·439	0·410	0·288	0·329	0·248	
2. English	0·439	(0·439)	0·351	0·354	0·320	0·329	
3. History	0·410	0·351	(0·410)	0·164	0·190	0·181	
4. Arithmetic	0·288	0·354	0·164	(0·595)	0·595	0·470	
5. Algebra	0·329	0·320	0·190	0·595	(0·595)	0·464	
6. Geometry	0·248	0·329	0·181	0·470	0·464	(0·470)	
Totals	2·153	2·232	1·706	2·466	2·493	2·162	Grand Total 13·212
$\sqrt{13{\cdot}212} = 3{\cdot}635$							
1st centroid loadings	0·592	0·614	0·469	0·678	0·686	0·595	Total 3·634

Table 3.2. First residual covariance matrix

	1	*2*	*3*	*4*	*5*	*6*
1	(0·086)	0·076	0·132	−0·113	−0·077	−0·104
2	0·076	(0·062)	0·063	−0·062	−0·101	−0·036
3	0·132	0·063	(0·190)	−0·154	−0·132	−0·098
4	−0·113	−0·062	−0·154	(0·135)	0·130	0·067
5	−0·077	−0·101	−0·132	0·130	(0·124)	0·056
6	−0·104	−0·036	−0·098	0·067	0·056	(0·116)

could be replaced by the largest entry in each column. The latter is the better procedure during the first iteration (but as a rule only in the first) for, if the original estimates of the communalities happened to be too small some of the entries in the diagonal cells of the residual matrix might be negative, and this cannot be allowed.

The residual matrix, with the signs of variates *4*, *5* and *6* reversed, and with new 'guesses' in the diagonal cells is given in Table 3.3.

The sums of the columns are given below the table, and when each of these is divided by the square root of the grand total of the matrix the first estimates of the loadings on the second centroid are obtained. Since our matrix contains only six variates there is no point in finding the loadings on a third centroid. The rule that $(p+k)$ should be less than $(p-k)^2$, which applied in the maximum likelihood method, and which sets an upper limit to k, applies here also. But if there were more variates a second residual matrix could be found by using the values in Table 3.3, and loadings on a third centroid obtained.

Finally the variates which had their signs reversed at each stage of the process must, at the very end, have them restored. In our example this means that the loadings for variates *4*, *5* and *6* on the second centroid, given at the bottom of Table 3.3 must be made negative. Moreover, had more than two centroid factors been extracted the signs of the loadings for these variates would also require to be reversed; and a similar process would be required for the variates reversed at each succeeding stage of the analysis.

Table 3.3. Residual matrix with signs reversed and new guessed communalities

	(0·132)	0·076	0·132	0·113	0·077	0·104	
	0·076	(0·101)	0·063	0·062	0·101	0·036	
	0·132	0·063	(0·154)	0·154	0·132	0·098	
	0·113	0·062	0·154	(0·154)	0·130	0·067	
	0·077	0·101	0·132	0·130	(0·124)	0·056	
	0·104	0·036	0·098	0·067	0·056	(0·104)	
Totals	0·634	0·439	0·733	0·680	0·628	0·465	Grand Total 3·579
			$\sqrt{3\cdot579} = 1\cdot892$				
Loadings on 2nd centroid	0·335	0·232	0·387	0·359	0·332	0·246	

Table 3.4. First estimates of centroid loadings

	Variate		
	1	*2*	*3*
1st centroid	0·592	0·614	0·469
2nd centroid	0·335	0·232	0·387
Communalities	0·463	0·431	0·370

	Variate		
	4	*5*	*6*
1st centroid	0·678	0·686	0·595
2nd centroid	−0·359	−0·332	−0·246
Communalities	0·589	0·581	0·415

Table 3.5. Second estimates of centroid loadings

	Variate		
	1	*2*	*3*
1st centroid	0·602	0·614	0·460
2nd centroid	0·330	0·208	0·389
Communalities	0·471	0·420	0·363

	Variate		
	4	*5*	*6*
1st centroid	0·680	0·684	0·582
2nd centroid	−0·359	−0·333	−0·235
Communalities	0·591	0·579	0·394

The loadings, with signs restored, on the two centroids are given in Table 3.4, together with new estimates of the communalities derived from them by adding together the squares of the loadings for each variate. Thus for variate *1* we have $0{\cdot}592^2+0{\cdot}335^2=0{\cdot}463$. To obtain more accurate estimates of the loadings these new communalities can be entered in the diagonal cells of the original matrix and the whole process repeated. After a further iteration the estimates in Table 3.5 are obtained.

3.5. Simplification of subsequent iterations

When the original matrix is large, the iterative process is tedious and in practice is seldom carried very far. But as soon as it is known what sign reflections are necessary at each stage, and this is generally the case after one iteration, the process can be simplified and speeded up considerably. As this is not widely known it will be illustrated in some detail. If the sign reflections are known in advance, a centroid analysis becomes a very simple matter.

The best way of representing the sign reversal process is to introduce a $p \times k$ matrix $\mathbf{Q}$ whose elements q_{ir} are all either $+1$ or -1. When all the correlations in the original matrix are positive the first column of $\mathbf{Q}$ will have each element equal to $+1$, but subsequent columns will have a fair proportion of elements equal to -1. As a rule, for non-zero loadings, q_{ir} will be the sign of l_{ir}, the loading of the ith variate on the rth centroid. We shall denote the covariance or correlation matrix with communalities in the diagonal cells by $\mathbf{A}_0$.

As a simple illustration let us suppose that $k = 2$, so that $\mathbf{Q}$ consists of two columns $\mathbf{q}_1$ and $\mathbf{q}_2$. Let the corresponding two columns of $\mathbf{L}$, the matrix of centroid loadings, be $\mathbf{l}_1$ and $\mathbf{l}_2$. Then the centroid method defines $\mathbf{l}_1$ by the equation

$$\tau_1 \mathbf{l}'_1 = \mathbf{q}'_1 \mathbf{A}_0, \tag{3.3}$$

where τ_1 is a scalar (assumed positive) satisfying

$$\tau_1 = \mathbf{q}'_1 \mathbf{l}_1, \qquad \tau_1^2 = \mathbf{q}'_1 \mathbf{A}_0 \mathbf{q}_1.$$

The residual matrix when the effect of the first factor has been removed is $(\mathbf{A}_0 - \mathbf{l}_1 \mathbf{l}'_1)$, and $\mathbf{l}_2$ may now be found by pre-multiplying this by $\mathbf{q}'_2$, giving

$$\tau_2 \mathbf{l}'_2 = \mathbf{q}'_2 (\mathbf{A}_0 - \mathbf{l}_1 \mathbf{l}'_1), \tag{3.4}$$

where τ_2 is a scalar (assumed positive) satisfying

$$\tau_2 = \mathbf{q}'_2\mathbf{l}_2, \quad \tau_2{}^2 = \mathbf{q}'_2(\mathbf{A}_0 - \mathbf{l}_1\mathbf{l}'_1)\mathbf{q}_2.$$

Post-multiplication of eq (3.4) by $\mathbf{q}_1$ and use of eq (3.3) establishes the fact that

$$\mathbf{l}'_2\mathbf{q}_1 = \mathbf{q}'_1\mathbf{l}_2 = 0. \tag{3.5}$$

A little examination shows that the eqs (3.3) and (3.4) may be combined into the single equation

$$\mathbf{TL} = \mathbf{Q}'\mathbf{A}_0, \tag{3.6}$$

where $\mathbf{T} = \mathbf{Q}'\mathbf{L}$, $\mathbf{TT}' = \mathbf{Q}'\mathbf{A}_0\mathbf{Q}$, and where in view of (3.5), $\mathbf{T}$ is a lower triangular matrix, i.e. a matrix in which all elements above the diagonal are zero. It is clear that this will be true for higher values of k. In general the procedure determines $\mathbf{L}$ uniquely.

If, as is assumed, $\mathbf{Q}$ is known, the centroid process can be carried out very much more conveniently than by the usual method of finding the residual matrix at each stage. For, after forming the $k \times k$ matrix $\mathbf{Q}'\mathbf{A}_0\mathbf{Q}$ it may easily be expressed in the form $\mathbf{TT}'$, where $\mathbf{T}$ is lower triangular with positive diagonal elements, and it is easy to form the inverse $\mathbf{T}^{-1}$, which is also lower triangular (see Appendix, p. 111). The matrix $\mathbf{L}$ may then be found by expressing eq (3.6) in the form

$$\mathbf{L}' = \mathbf{T}^{-1}\mathbf{Q}'\mathbf{A}_0. \tag{3.7}$$

In our example we have

$$\mathbf{Q}' = \begin{bmatrix} 1 & 1 & 1 & 1 & 1 & 1 \\ 1 & 1 & 1 & -1 & -1 & -1 \end{bmatrix},$$

and $\mathbf{A}_0$ may be taken firstly as the correlation matrix with the communalities given in Table 3.5 as diagonal elements. The matrices $\mathbf{Q}'\mathbf{A}_0$ and $\mathbf{Q}'\mathbf{A}_0\mathbf{Q}$ are found to be respectively

$$\begin{bmatrix} 2{\cdot}185 & 2{\cdot}213 & 1{\cdot}659 & 2{\cdot}462 & 2{\cdot}477 & 2{\cdot}086 \\ 0{\cdot}455 & 0{\cdot}207 & 0{\cdot}589 & -0{\cdot}850 & -0{\cdot}799 & -0{\cdot}570 \end{bmatrix}$$

and

$$\begin{bmatrix} 13{\cdot}082 & -0{\cdot}968 \\ -0{\cdot}968 & 3{\cdot}470 \end{bmatrix}.$$

If $\mathbf{T}$ is denoted by $\begin{bmatrix} a & 0 \\ b & c \end{bmatrix}$, then $\mathbf{TT}' = \begin{bmatrix} a^2 & ab \\ ab & b^2+c^2 \end{bmatrix}$.

Hence $a^2 = 13{\cdot}082$, $ab = -0{\cdot}968$, $b^2+c^2 = 3{\cdot}470$, and we obtain successively

$$a = 3{\cdot}6169, \quad b = -0{\cdot}2676, \quad c = 1{\cdot}8435.$$

Again if $\mathbf{T}^{-1}$ is denoted by $\begin{bmatrix} x & 0 \\ y & z \end{bmatrix}$, then

$$\mathbf{TT}^{-1} = \begin{bmatrix} a & 0 \\ b & c \end{bmatrix}\begin{bmatrix} x & 0 \\ y & z \end{bmatrix} = \begin{bmatrix} 1 & 0 \\ 0 & 1 \end{bmatrix};$$

so that $ax = 1$, $cz = 1$ and $bx+cy = 0$.
Hence $x = 0{\cdot}2765$, $z = 0{\cdot}5424$ and $y = 0{\cdot}0401$.
From eq (3.7) the new estimates of the centroid loadings and the communalities are found to be as in Table 3.6.

Table 3.6. Third estimates of centroid loadings

	Variate		
	1	*2*	*3*
1st centroid	0·604	0·612	0·459
2nd centroid	0·334	0·201	0·386
Communalities	0·476	0·415	0·360

	Variate		
	4	*5*	*6*
1st centroid	0·681	0·685	0·577
2nd centroid	−0·362	−0·334	−0·226
Communalities	0·595	0·581	0·384

After a further iteration is performed, using these new estimates of the communalities in $\mathbf{A}_0$, the loadings show signs of convergence. They are given in Table 3.7.

Table 3.7. Fourth estimates of centroid loadings

	Variate		
	1	*2*	*3*
1st centroid	0·606	0·611	0·458
2nd centroid	0·337	0·197	0·384
Communalities	0·481	0·412	0·357

	Variate		
	4	*5*	*6*
1st centroid	0·683	0·686	0·575
2nd centroid	−0·365	−0·335	−0·221
Communalities	0·600	0·583	0·379

The amount of the total variance of the six variates extracted by each centroid can now be obtained by taking the sum of the squares of the loadings on each. For the first centroid this gives 2·218, which, when expressed as a percentage of the total variance of 6, is 37 per cent. Corresponding figures for the second centroid are 0·594, or 10 per cent.

3.6. Efficiency of estimation and tests of significance

The efficiency of the centroid method, as generally practised, is difficult to assess partly because of the necessity of estimating the communalities and partly because correlation coefficients, rather than covariances, are usually employed. The problem is also complicated to some extent by the arbitrariness of the sign changing. The efficiency of a modified version of the method in which

(*a*) the residual variances are assumed to be known,

(*b*) the covariance matrix is used,

(*c*) the sign changes are determined in advance

has been investigated (Lawley, 1955). Under these conditions it was found that the efficiency of the method was generally high.

For the modified version a criterion of large-sample χ^2 type was derived for testing the significance of the residuals after k centroid factors had been eliminated. The criterion may be expressed as

$$\tfrac{1}{2}n\ \mathrm{tr}(\mathbf{X}^2), \tag{3.8}$$

where

$$\mathbf{X} = (\mathbf{V}^{-1}-\mathbf{V}^{-1}\mathbf{L}\mathbf{J}^{-1}\mathbf{L}'\mathbf{V}^{-1})(\mathbf{A}-\mathbf{C});$$

and the number of degrees of freedom is $\frac{1}{2}(p-k)(p-k+1)$. The notation here is that of Chapter 2. As before, $\mathbf{V}$ is the diagonal matrix whose elements are the residual variances, $\mathbf{J} = \mathbf{L}'\mathbf{V}^{-1}\mathbf{L}$ (in general, not diagonal) and $\mathbf{C} = \mathbf{L}\mathbf{L}'+\mathbf{V}$. In practice estimated values have to be substituted for the unknown parameters, but for simplicity we omit circumflex accents. Since

$$\mathbf{A}-\mathbf{C} = \mathbf{A}-\mathbf{V}-\mathbf{L}\mathbf{L}' = \mathbf{A}_0-\mathbf{L}\mathbf{L}',$$

we have, alternatively,

$$\begin{aligned}\mathbf{X} &= (\mathbf{V}^{-1}-\mathbf{V}^{-1}\mathbf{L}\mathbf{J}^{-1}\mathbf{L}'\mathbf{V}^{-1})\mathbf{A}_0 \\ &= \mathbf{V}^{-1}(\mathbf{A}_0-\mathbf{L}\mathbf{M}'),\end{aligned} \tag{3.9}$$

where $\mathbf{M}' = \mathbf{J}^{-1}\mathbf{L}'\mathbf{V}^{-1}\mathbf{A}_0$. (3.10)

It seems likely that the centroid method, without the above modifications, has reasonably high efficiency, but no entirely satisfactory test of significance has been devised, even for large samples. The best suggestion is probably that the criterion of (3.8) should still be treated as an approximate χ^2 variate, but that the number of degrees of freedom should be reduced by p to allow for the estimation of the residual variances. This is not entirely legitimate since the estimates of the residual variances are not fully efficient. The number of degrees of freedom now becomes

$$\tfrac{1}{2}\{(p-k)^2-(p+k)\},$$

the same as for the χ^2 test of Chapter 2. The adequacy of the approximation depends not only on the sample being a large one but also on there being a moderately large number of degrees of freedom for χ^2.

The best method of evaluating the criterion is to calculate successively the matrices $\mathbf{L}'\mathbf{V}^{-1}$, $\mathbf{J}$, $\mathbf{L}'\mathbf{V}^{-1}\mathbf{A}_0$ and $\mathbf{M}'$, as given

4

by (3.10). We then find $\mathbf{X} = [x_{ij}]$ from (3.9). This is arithmetically more convenient than direct use of the matrix of residuals. The matrix $\mathbf{A}_0 - \mathbf{LM}'$ is analogous to the residual matrix, but is not symmetric and its diagonal elements are not necessarily zero. The criterion of (3.8) may finally be calculated in the form

$$n(\tfrac{1}{2}\sum_{i} x_{ii}^2 + \sum_{i<j} x_{ij}x_{ji}). \tag{3.11}$$

For the numerical data of this chapter we may test whether the residuals after eliminating two centroid factors are significant. We have $n = 219$, $p = 6$ and $k = 2$. The value of χ^2 is found to be 2·5, which, with 4 degrees of freedom, is below expectation. With so few degrees of freedom the test must of course be regarded with suspicion, but taken at its face value it would lead us to accept the hypothesis that only two common factors are required to account for the correlations.

In general, when the criterion is either well below or well above the chosen significance level it is safe to accept or reject the hypothesis. In borderline cases a test based on maximum likelihood estimation would be necessary to reach a firmer decision.

Exercises

1. Using unities in the diagonal cells, show that the loadings on the three centroids derived from analysing the correlation matrix

1·0	0·8	0·6
0·8	1·0	0·7
0·6	0·7	1·0

are as follows:

I	II	III
0·895	0·324	−0·309
0·932	0·191	0·309
0·857	−0·515	0·000

Check the calculations by post-multiplying the matrix of loadings by its transpose.

2. The following matrix gives the correlations for a sample of 148 children on 13 variates. The first five variates are measures of orectic tendency, the next three are measures of cognitive ability, while the remainder are measures of manual dexterity and reaction time.

Correlation matrix for thirteen variates

1	*2*	*3*	*4*	*5*	*6*	*7*	*8*	*9*	*10*	*11*	*12*	*13*
1·00	0·44	0·33	0·39	0·33	−0·13	−0·01	0·00	0·04	−0·02	−0·05	0·13	0·06
	1·00	0·37	0·48	0·40	−0·27	−0·23	−0·15	−0·03	0·00	−0·07	0·07	0·05
		1·00	0·52	0·22	−0·23	−0·07	−0·13	0·05	−0·02	0·05	0·10	0·06
			1·00	0·28	−0·10	0·02	−0·05	−0·01	0·08	0·03	0·02	0·04
				1·00	−0·21	−0·16	−0·03	0·00	0·04	0·09	0·03	0·01
					1·00	0·60	0·55	0·20	−0·16	0·03	−0·31	−0·22
						1·00	0·56	0·29	−0·28	−0·18	−0·21	−0·18
							1·00	0·51	−0·16	0·00	−0·22	−0·19
								1·00	−0·09	0·08	−0·22	−0·29
									1·00	0·08	0·12	0·09
										1·00	−0·15	−0·08
											1·00	0·65
												1·00

Show that the number of negative signs in the complete matrix can be reduced to a minimum either by reversing the signs of variates *6*, *7*, *8* and *9* or of variates *6*, *7*, *8*, *9* and *11*, and that when the magnitudes of the correlations are taken into account the latter alternative is slightly preferable. By inserting the largest correlation in each column in the diagonal cell of that column, show that the loadings on the first centroid, before the signs are restored, are as follows:

0·40 0·55 0·44 0·44 0·36 0·65 0·54 0·56 0·39
0·21 0·04 0·52 0·46

REFERENCES

Burt, C. (1940), *The Factors of the Mind*, London University Press

Jowett, G. H. (1958), Factor analysis, *Appl. Statist.* **7,** 114–125

Lawley, D. N. (1955), A statistical examination of the centroid method, *Proc. Roy. Soc. Edin.* **A64,** 175–189

Thomson, G. H. (1951), *The Factorial Analysis of Human Ability*, London University Press

Thomson, G. H. (1954), *The Geometry of Mental Measurement*, London University Press

Thurstone, L. L. (1947), *Multiple Factor Analysis*, Chicago University Press

4
THE METHOD OF PRINCIPAL COMPONENTS

4.1. Introduction

The main points of difference between factor analysis and principal component analysis have already been noted in Chapter 1. Since the latter method is relatively well known only a brief account of it need be given here. In it a linear transformation is applied to the p observed variates $x_1, x_2, ..., x_p$, to produce a new set of uncorrelated and standardized variates $z_1, z_2, ..., z_p$; but no hypothesis need be made regarding the x's. As Burt (1949) has pointed out this method had effectively been put forward by Karl Pearson in 1901, but the procedures in general use are due to Hotelling (1933).

4.2. Basic equations

In principal component analysis the basic equations are

$$x_i = \sum_{r=1}^{p} w_{ir} z_r \quad (i, r = 1, 2, ..., p), \tag{4.1}$$

where z_r stands for the rth component and w_{ir} is the weight of the rth component in the ith variate. On comparing eqs (4.1) with those of (1.1) it is seen that no residual terms e_i are considered, for in a principal component analysis the total variance of the variates is accounted for when all p components are found.

In matrix notation the eqs (4.1) may be written

$$\mathbf{x} = \mathbf{W}\mathbf{z}, \tag{4.2}$$

where

$$\mathbf{x} = \{x_1\, x_2\, ...\, x_p\},$$

$$\mathbf{z} = \{z_1\, z_2\, ...\, z_p\}$$

and

$$\mathbf{W} = [w_{ir}].$$

We first transform to new variates $y_1, y_2, ..., y_p$ satisfying

$$\mathbf{y} = \mathbf{U}'\mathbf{x}, \quad \mathbf{x} = \mathbf{U}\mathbf{y}, \tag{4.3}$$

where $\mathbf{y} = \{y_1\, y_2\, ...\, y_p\}$ and $\mathbf{U}$ is an orthogonal matrix. Let $\mathbf{u}_r$ denote the rth column of $\mathbf{U}$ (and $\mathbf{u}'_r$ the rth row of $\mathbf{U}'$).

Then $\mathbf{u}_1$ is chosen first in such a way that the variance of y_1 is maximized. When this is done, $\mathbf{u}_2$ is chosen so that the variance of y_2 is maximized, subject to the condition that y_2 is uncorrelated with y_1. Similarly for the remaining y's. The variance of y_r is maximized subject to the condition that y_r is uncorrelated with $y_1, y_2, ..., y_{r-1}$.

Let us denote the variance of y_r by λ_r. As before the sample covariance matrix of the x's is denoted by $\mathbf{A}$. Since $y_r = \mathbf{u}'_r\mathbf{x}$, we have

$$\lambda_r = \mathbf{u}'_r\mathbf{A}\mathbf{u}_r,$$

and, as the y's are uncorrelated, we have also

$$\mathbf{u}'_r\mathbf{A}\mathbf{u}_s = 0, \quad \text{for } r \neq s.$$

This means that the matrix

$$\mathbf{U}'\mathbf{A}\mathbf{U} = \mathbf{\Lambda} \tag{4.4}$$

is diagonal with elements $\lambda_1, \lambda_2, ..., \lambda_p$, arranged in order of magnitude. We suppose them to be unequal, as is usually the case in practice. In fact λ_r is the rth latent root of $\mathbf{A}$, in order of magnitude, and $\mathbf{u}'_r$ is the corresponding latent row vector, which satisfies

$$\mathbf{u}'_r\mathbf{A} = \lambda_r\mathbf{u}'_r.$$

The rth principal component z_r is obtained by standardizing y_r. To make the variance of z_r unity we put, for $r = 1, 2, ..., p$,

$$z_r = \lambda_r^{-\frac{1}{2}}y_r = \lambda_r^{-\frac{1}{2}}\mathbf{u}'_r\mathbf{x}.$$

In matrix notation this becomes

$$\mathbf{z} = \mathbf{\Lambda}^{-\frac{1}{2}}\mathbf{y} = \mathbf{\Lambda}^{-\frac{1}{2}}\mathbf{U}'\mathbf{x}. \tag{4.5}$$

These equations express the z_r in terms of the x_i. To find the x_i in terms of z_r we pre-multiply in eq (4.5) by $\mathbf{U}\mathbf{\Lambda}^{\frac{1}{2}}$. This gives

$$\mathbf{x} = \mathbf{U}\mathbf{\Lambda}^{\frac{1}{2}}\mathbf{z}$$

which is identical with (4.2) if we put

$$\mathbf{W} = \mathbf{U}\mathbf{\Lambda}^{\frac{1}{2}}. \tag{4.6}$$

The rth column of $\mathbf{W}$ is

$$\mathbf{w}_r = \lambda_r^{\frac{1}{2}}\mathbf{u}_r$$

and the scale of $\mathbf{w}_r$ is determined by $\mathbf{w}'_r\mathbf{w}_r = \lambda_r$.

By the use of eqs (4.4.) and (4.6) it is easy to see that $\mathbf{WW}' = \mathbf{A}$, and that $\mathbf{W}'\mathbf{W} = \mathbf{\Lambda}$. Since $\mathrm{tr}(\mathbf{A}) = \mathrm{tr}(\mathbf{\Lambda})$, the total variance of the variates x_i is equal to that of the unstandardized components y_r. We are thus able to find the proportion of the total variance contributed by each component.

In performing numerical calculations it is often convenient to alter the scale of a vector $\mathbf{u}_r$, and then $\mathbf{u}'_r\mathbf{u}_r$ is no longer unity. In this case it is $(\mathbf{u}'_r\mathbf{A}\mathbf{u}_r)/(\mathbf{u}'_r\mathbf{u}_r)$ which is maximized and made equal to λ_r.

4.3. Discussion of method

Principal component analysis is most useful when the variates x_i are all measured in the same units. If they are not, the method is more difficult to justify. A change in the scales of measurement of some or all of the variates results in the covariance matrix being multiplied on both sides by a diagonal matrix. The effect of this on the latent roots and vectors is very complicated, and the components are unfortunately not invariant under such changes of scale. In this respect principal component analysis contrasts unfavourably with the method of factor analysis given in Chapter 2. One advantage which it does, however, have over the method of Chapter 2 is that the convergence of the iterative procedure involved is in general very much faster.

In educational and psychological work it is a common practice to standardize each variate. The covariance matrix $\mathbf{A}$ is then replaced by the matrix $\mathbf{R}$ of correlations. This raises difficulties when tests of significance are required, a fact which has not always been sufficiently appreciated. Though a correlation matrix is used in the example below this should not be taken as an endorsement of the procedure.

4.4. Numerical evaluation of weights

Nowadays the latent roots and vectors of a matrix are often found on electronic computers. Several different methods of calculating them are available and a programmer is likely to adopt the method best suited to his computer. The method below is that given by Hotelling and is employed here primarily to illustrate the general pattern of the analysis.

To illustrate the calculations, the correlations, Table 4.1, between five psychophysical measures for a sample of 123 individuals will be used.

Table 4.1. Correlation matrix **R** for five psychophysical measures

	1	*2*	*3*	*4*	*5*
1	1·000	0·438	−0·137	0·205	−0·178
2	0·438	1·000	0·031	0·180	−0·304
3	−0·137	0·031	1·000	0·161	0·372
4	0·205	0·180	0·161	1·000	−0·013
5	−0·178	−0·304	0·372	−0·013	1·000
Total	1·328	1·345	1·427	1·533	0·877

To begin the calculations a trial vector $\mathbf{u}'_{(1)}$ is chosen and the correlation matrix **R** is pre-multiplied by it. Any values for the elements of $\mathbf{u}'_{(1)}$ could be chosen, but it is frequently the case that values roughly proportional to the column totals of the matrix give fairly good initial approximations; so we shall take the values of $\mathbf{u}'_{(1)}$ to be

$$[0{\cdot}9 \quad 0{\cdot}9 \quad 1{\cdot}0 \quad 1{\cdot}0 \quad 0{\cdot}7].$$

In this example $\mathbf{u}'_{(1)}$ happens to be a very bad approximation, due to the presence of several negative correlation coefficients, and the ensuing iterative procedure takes an unduly long time to converge. Two elements eventually change sign. We first find

$$\mathbf{u}'_{(1)}\mathbf{R} = [1{\cdot}238 \quad 1{\cdot}292 \quad 1{\cdot}326 \quad 1{\cdot}498 \quad 0{\cdot}625].$$

The largest entry is 1·498, and when each element of $\mathbf{u}'_{(1)}\mathbf{R}$ is divided by this value a new trial vector, which we will denote by $\mathbf{u}'_{(2)}$, is obtained. It is

$$\mathbf{u}'_{(2)} = [0{\cdot}826 \quad 0{\cdot}862 \quad 0{\cdot}885 \quad 1{\cdot}000 \quad 0{\cdot}417].$$

Pre-multiplying **R** by the latter vector we obtain

$$\mathbf{u}'_{(2)}\mathbf{R} = [1{\cdot}217 \quad 1{\cdot}304 \quad 1{\cdot}085 \quad 1{\cdot}457 \quad 0{\cdot}313].$$

When each element in this vector is divided by the largest element, namely 1·457, a new trial vector $\mathbf{u}'_{(3)}$ is obtained. It is

$$\mathbf{u}'_{(3)} = [0{\cdot}835 \quad 0{\cdot}895 \quad 0{\cdot}745 \quad 1{\cdot}000 \quad 0{\cdot}215].$$

The process is continued in this way until the elements of the vector $\mathbf{u'R}$ converge to stationary values. In our case these values are given by

$$\mathbf{u'R} = [1{\cdot}729 \quad 1{\cdot}757 \quad -0{\cdot}840 \quad 0{\cdot}734 \quad -1{\cdot}536].$$

The largest element is now 1·757. It is the first latent root, λ_1, of the matrix $\mathbf{R}$, and when all the elements of $\mathbf{u'R}$ are divided by this value the first latent vector $\mathbf{u'}_1$ is obtained. It is

$$\mathbf{u'}_1 = [0{\cdot}984 \quad 1{\cdot}000 \quad -0{\cdot}478 \quad 0{\cdot}418 \quad -0{\cdot}874].$$

The first column of $\mathbf{W}$ is now obtained by multiplying $\mathbf{u}_1$ by the scalar quantity $\lambda_1^{\frac{1}{2}}(\mathbf{u'}_1\mathbf{u}_1)^{-\frac{1}{2}}$. The vector product $\mathbf{u'}_1\mathbf{u}_1$ is 3·135. Hence the scalar is $\sqrt{(1{\cdot}757/3{\cdot}135)} = 0{\cdot}7485$, and the first column of $\mathbf{W}$ is

$$\mathbf{w}_1 = \{0{\cdot}737 \quad 0{\cdot}749 \quad -0{\cdot}358 \quad 0{\cdot}313 \quad -0{\cdot}654\}.$$

This calculation may be checked by verifying that $\mathbf{w'}_1\mathbf{w}_1 = \lambda_1$.

To obtain the second latent root and corresponding latent vector of the matrix $\mathbf{R}$, the residual matrix, after the effect of the first principal component has been removed, must be obtained. It is given by the expression $\mathbf{R}-\mathbf{w}_1\mathbf{w'}_1$ and appears in Table 4.2.

Table 4.2. First residual matrix

	1	*2*	*3*	*4*	*5*
1	0·456	−0·114	0·127	−0·025	0·304
2	−0·114	0·439	0·299	−0·054	0·186
3	0·127	0·299	0·872	0·273	0·138
4	−0·025	−0·054	0·273	0·902	0·192
5	0·304	0·186	0·138	0·192	0·572

Guesses at the values of the elements of the second latent vector, $\mathbf{u'}_2$, are now made and the same process as was carried out when $\mathbf{u'}_1$ was being found is repeated.

The five latent roots and corresponding vectors for the matrix $\mathbf{R}$ are given in Table 4.3.

Table 4.3. Latent roots and vectors of **R**

Roots	*Vectors*					
$\lambda_1 = 1{\cdot}757$	$\mathbf{u}'_1$	0·984	1·000	−0·478	0·418	−0·874
$\lambda_2 = 1{\cdot}331$	$\mathbf{u}'_2$	0·281	0·374	1·000	0·841	0·598
$\lambda_3 = 0{\cdot}781$	$\mathbf{u}'_3$	−0·272	−0·560	−0·408	1·000	−0·245
$\lambda_4 = 0{\cdot}709$	$\mathbf{u}'_4$	1·000	−0·478	−0·621	−0·028	0·905
$\lambda_5 = 0{\cdot}422$	$\mathbf{u}'_5$	−0·777	1·000	−0·828	0·213	0·825

The sum of the roots is equal to 5, which is the trace of the matrix **R**.

In Table 4.4 the matrix **W** of weights for the five components, I to V, derived from the vectors in Table 4.3 by applying the scalar multiplier $\lambda_r^{\frac{1}{2}}(\mathbf{u}'_r\mathbf{u}_r)^{-\frac{1}{2}}$, are shown (columns of **W** correspond to rows of Table 4.3).

Table 4.4

Variates	*Components*				
	I	II	III	IV	V
1	0·737	0·214	−0·188	0·540	−0·291
2	0·749	0·285	−0·390	−0·258	0·374
3	−0·358	0·764	−0·284	−0·335	−0·310
4	0·313	0·642	0·695	−0·015	0·080
5	−0·654	0·457	−0·171	0·489	0·309
Percentage variance	35·1	26·6	15·6	14·2	8·4

An overall check on the calculations can now be made by verifying that $\mathbf{WW}' = \mathbf{R}$. Various methods have been suggested for accelerating the convergence of the above procedure. See, for example, a paper by Aitken (1937).

For our example eqs (4.1) can now be written in detail. For instance x_1 is given by

$$x_1 = 0{\cdot}737z_1 + 0{\cdot}214z_2 - 0{\cdot}188z_3 + 0{\cdot}540z_4 - 0{\cdot}291z_5.$$

Conversely, the component scores can be written in terms of the variate scores. For example z_1 is given by

$$z_1 = (0{\cdot}737x_1 + 0{\cdot}749x_2 - \ldots - 0{\cdot}654x_5) \div 1{\cdot}757,$$

where 1·757 is the first latent root.

4.5. Tests of significance

In principal component analysis it is common practice, especially if p is fairly large, to evaluate only the first few, say k, latent roots and vectors. The process may reasonably be stopped when the components already found account for a sufficiently high proportion of the total variance. Criteria have, however, been suggested by Bartlett (1951, 1954) for testing the hypothesis that the population values of the $p-k$ smallest roots are equal. This hypothesis, if true, implies that every linear function

$$\sum_i l_i x_i$$

satisfying

$$\sum_i l_i^2 = 1$$

and uncorrelated with $y_1, y_2, \ldots, y_k$ has the same population variance. There is then no point in maximizing the variances of $y_{k+1}, \ldots, y_p$, and these variates, if required, may be chosen in any way which satisfies the orthogonality relations (4.3).

Let us consider first the relatively simple case where $k = 0$ and the hypothesis is that the true values of all p latent roots are equal. If we are testing the significance of the differences between the latent roots of an *unstandardized* sample covariance matrix $\mathbf{A}$, the appropriate criterion is

$$\{n-\tfrac{1}{6}(2p+1+2/p)\}\{-\log_e |\mathbf{A}|+p \log_e (\operatorname{tr} \mathbf{A}/p)\}. \tag{4.7}$$

For moderately large values of n (and normally distributed x_i) this is distributed approximately as χ^2 with $\frac{1}{2}(p+2)(p-1)$ degrees of freedom. If, on the other hand, all variates have been standardized, the covariance matrix is in effect replaced by the correlation matrix $\mathbf{R}$. The correct criterion is then

$$-\{n-\tfrac{1}{6}(2p+5)\} \log_e |\mathbf{R}|, \tag{4.8}$$

which is distributed approximately as χ^2 with $\frac{1}{2}p(p-1)$ degrees of freedom.

Now suppose that k (>0) latent roots have been eliminated and that we wish to test the significance of the differences between the residual $p-k$ roots (we suppose $p-k \geqslant 2$). If we are dealing witn an unstandardized covariance matrix, we use as an approximate χ^2 criterion

$$n'\{-\log_e |\mathbf{A}|+\log_e (\lambda_1 \ldots \lambda_k)+q \log_e \lambda\}, \tag{4.9}$$

where

$$q = p-k,$$
$$\lambda = (\operatorname{tr} \mathbf{A}-\lambda_1- \ldots -\lambda_k)/q.$$

With sufficient accuracy we may take n' as given by

$$n' = n-k-\tfrac{1}{6}(2q+1+2/q),$$

though there is some evidence (Lawley, 1956) that the approximation is slightly improved if this value is increased by an amount

$$\lambda^2 \sum_{r=1}^{k} 1/(\lambda_r-\lambda)^2.$$

The number of degrees of freedom for χ^2 is in this case $\frac{1}{2}(p-k+2)\,(p-k-1)$.

In the corresponding test for the standardized case, where **A** is replaced by **R**, considerable difficulties arise. The criterion suggested is

$$n\{-\log_e|\mathbf{R}|+\log_e(\lambda_1 \dots \lambda_k)+(p-k)\log_e\lambda\}, \qquad (4.10)$$

where λ is now given by

$$\lambda = (p-\lambda_1-\dots-\lambda_k)/(p-k).$$

Unfortunately, even in the limit, when $n \to \infty$, this criterion does not have an exact χ^2 distribution. For this reason we have taken the multiplying factor simply as n, a more accurate value being scarcely justified. The expectation of the criterion (4.10), which may be treated as the effective number of degrees of freedom for χ^2, is in general a somewhat complicated expression. If the eliminated latent roots account for a fairly high proportion of the total variance, it may, however, be taken as approximately $\frac{1}{2}(p-k+2)(p-k-1)$, the same as the number of degrees of freedom in the unstandardized case.

To illustrate the use of the tests involving **R** we shall apply them to the data of our numerical example. If we first test the significance of the differences between all five roots, we have $n = 122$, $p = 5$, $n-\frac{1}{6}(2p+5) = 119{\cdot}5$, and

$$|\mathbf{R}| = \lambda_1\lambda_2 \dots \lambda_5 = 0{\cdot}5465.$$

From expression (4.8) we then obtain a value for χ^2 of $72{\cdot}2$, with 10 degrees of freedom. The value is highly significant, as might have been expected.

Since the first two latent roots are much larger than the rest, let us eliminate them and test the significance of the differences between the three smallest roots. In this case we have

$k = 2$, $\lambda_1 = 1{\cdot}757$, $\lambda_2 = 1{\cdot}331$ and $\lambda = 0{\cdot}6373$. Expression (4.10) then gives a value for χ^2 of 12·5. If we take the number of degrees of freedom to be 5, this value is significant at the 5 per cent level.

Exercises

1. Show that the first four latent roots of the 9×9 correlation matrix given in Table 2.1 are respectively 4·677, 1·262, 0·840 and 0·556 and that the weights for the first four principal components are as follows:

I	0·748	0·761	0·595	0·792	0·679	0·748	0·755	0·521	0·833
II	−0·266	−0·120	−0·293	0·453	0·565	0·509	−0·304	−0·366	−0·284
III	0·113	−0·263	−0·500	0·048	−0·059	0·177	−0·081	0·681	−0·016
IV	−0·256	−0·160	0·536	0·083	0·001	0·071	−0·247	0·303	−0·111

2. The determinant of the matrix referred to in exercise 1 has the value 0·0088762. Show that differences between the remaining roots, after the first three latent roots have been removed, are highly significant. The sample size is 211. ($\chi^2 = 76{\cdot}2$, with 20 degrees of freedom. Note that this result contrasts with that of the significance test of Chapter 2, when three factors had been eliminated.)

REFERENCES

Aitken, A. C. (1937), The evaluation of the latent roots and vectors of a matrix, *Proc. Roy. Soc. Edin.* **57**, 269–304

Bartlett, M. S. (1951), The effect of standardization on an approximation in factor analysis, *Biometrika* **38**, 337–344

Bartlett, M. S. (1954), A note on the multiplying factor for various χ^2 approximations, *J. Roy. Statist. Soc.* **B16**, 296–298

Burt, C. (1949), Alternative methods of factor analysis and their relation to Pearson's method of principal axes, *Brit. J. Psychol. Statist. Sect.* **2**, 98–121

Hotelling, H. (1933), Analysis of a complex of statistical variables into principal components, *J. Educ. Psychol.* **24**, 417–441, 498–520

Lawley, D. N. (1956), Tests of significance for the latent roots of covariance and correlation matrices, *Biometrika* **43**, 128–136

5

FACTOR ROTATION AND INTERPRETATION

5.1. Introduction

Once a set of factor loadings or component weights, corresponding to a set of hypothetical variates, has been found the next step is to try to interpret them in a way which will give a meaningful summary of the original data. As a first step let us take the results of the analysis in Chapter 3 in which the loadings for the six variates, 1, Gaelic; 2, English; 3, History; 4, Arithmetic; 5, Algebra; 6, Geometry; on two factors were found. They are repeated here (Table 5.1) for convenience.

Table 5.1. Factor loadings in six school subjects

	1	*2*	*3*	*4*	*5*	*6*	*Variance* (%)
Factor I	0·606	0·611	0·458	0·683	0·686	0·575	37·0
Factor II	0·337	0·197	0·384	−0·365	−0·335	−0·221	9·9
Communalities	0·481	0·412	0·357	0·600	0·583	0·379	46·9

The fact that all the correlations (Table 3.1) between the variates are positive indicates that students who get scores above average on any one of the subjects tend also to get scores above average on the other subjects. This reflection of the overall response of individuals to instruction, and of their relative facilities for acquiring knowledge, is variously referred to as their 'educability' or 'intelligence'. Now the first factor, on which all the loadings are positive, accounts for this feature of the data and so might be labelled 'general intelligence'. When its effect is eliminated from the correlation matrix the residuals (cf. Table 3.2) reflect a contrast

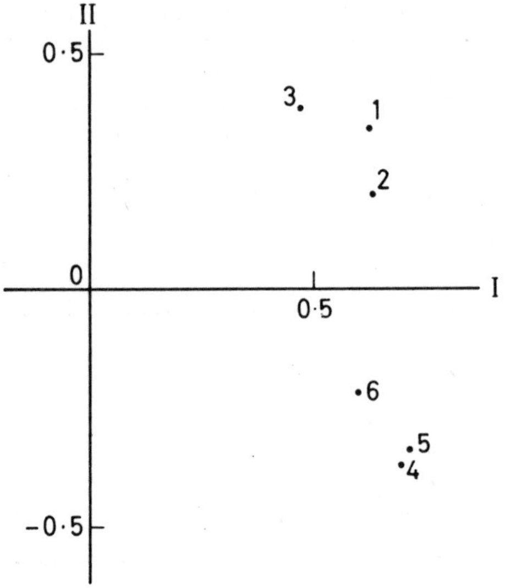

FIG. 5.1

between the first three and the last three variates. This contrast is seen in the second factor (Table 5.1) where the signs of the loadings for the two sets of variates are different.

A factor on which roughly half the loadings are positive and half negative is termed a bi-polar factor. (It is immaterial which pole is taken to be positive, for the signs of the loadings on the factor can be reversed without alteration of the analysis.) In our example the bi-polar factor reflects a contrast between the three verbal-type subjects, Gaelic, English and History, and the three mathematical subjects, Arithmetic, Algebra and Geometry. The variate which this bi-polar factor represents is such that individuals who get above average scores on the verbal subjects would tend to have above average scores on it, and individuals who get above average scores on the mathematical subjects would tend to have scores below average on it. What the analysis has demonstrated is that, at a given level of general intelligence, individuals who do well on verbal subjects tend to do less well on mathematical subjects, and *vice versa*. Scores for students on the hypothetical variates or factors can also be obtained (Chapter 7). In this way the students can be ranked in order of merit on each.

Another way of looking at the data in Table 5.1, which is informative, is to plot the test-points in a diagram in which orthogonal axes are taken to represent the factors and the coordinates of the points are the factor loadings. This is done in Figure 5.1, and it is seen that the points appear to lie in two clusters which subtend an acute angle at the origin. The possibility then exists of interpreting the results in terms of two oblique, or correlated, factors: one 'verbal' in content and the other 'mathematical'. The general factor will now be submerged in these (see exercise 1 at the end of this chapter). Correlated factors are fairly widely used in factorial work in psychology and education (Thurstone, 1947; Cattell, 1952), and methods of estimating the correlations between them and the loadings on them will be discussed later. Before doing so it is necessary to consider the question of factor rotation.

5.2. A method of rotating factors

Previously it has been shown that the set of loadings obtained from a factor analysis, when the number of common factors exceeds one, is not unique and that other equivalent sets can be derived by orthogonal transformations of it. This fact is frequently utilized in an effort to simplify the results of an analysis, and to make them more meaningful—even if it does allow different interpretations of the same data to be given. To illustrate the rotation procedure a further example will be valuable.

Table 5.2 gives the maximum likelihood loadings for three factors obtained from an analysis of the correlation coefficients between the scores of a sample of 292 children on a set of 10 cognitive tests. The titles of the tests appear in the table and are more or less self-explanatory. Since all the correlations were positive the first factor could, without further discussion, be taken to be one of general intelligence. But when we come to factors II_0 and III_0 interpretation is not immediately obvious, and is rendered difficult by the presence of a relatively large number of negative and rather small loadings. It will be well then to examine the results more closely and to see if they can be clarified.

Table 5.2. Factor loadings for a set of cognitive tests

Tests	*Factors*			
	I_0	II_0	III_0	*Communalities*
1. Comprehension	0·788	−0·152	−0·352	0·768
2. Arithmetic	0·874	0·381	0·041	0·911
3. Similarities	0·814	−0·043	−0·213	0·710
4. Vocabulary	0·798	−0·170	−0·204	0·707
5. Digit span	0·641	0·070	−0·042	0·418
6. Picture completion	0·755	−0·298	0·067	0·663
7. Picture arrangement	0·782	−0·221	0·028	0·661
8. Block design	0·767	−0·091	0·358	0·725
9. Object assembly	0·733	−0·384	0·229	0·737
10. Coding	0·771	−0·101	0·071	0·610
Percentage variances	60·0	5·1	4·0	69·1

The ideal way of doing this would be to make a three-dimensional model in which three orthogonal axes are taken to represent the factors. The tests could then be represented in the space by points whose coordinates were equal to the loadings of the tests on the factors. Once this model has been made the actual axes employed could temporarily be forgotten and attention concentrated on the real point of interest, namely the positions of the test-points relative to each other in the space. Though the axes may be rotated about their origin, or may be allowed to become oblique, the distribution of the points will remain invariant. When it is examined the points may be found to lie in clusters, or perhaps to be concentrated in one or two octants of the space. If this were so it would then be reasonable to anchor the axes in a way which would allow the positions of the points to be described as simply as possible, that is, using as few parameters or loadings as possible.

Since a three-dimensional model is not possible here, in any case would be inadequate when the number of factors was greater than three, we must content ourselves by looking at the factors two at a time. When three factors are concerned three plots can be obtained, but, as a beginning, let us look at the plot of factors I_0 and III_0 (Figure 5.2(*a*)).

Examination of the figure shows that if the axes are given an orthogonal rotation in a clockwise direction, so that the first factor is made to pass through test-point 1, then all the test-points will lie in the first quadrant and all the signs of the loadings will become positive. In their new positions the factors will be denoted by I_1 and III_1 and it will be clear that I_1 can still be labelled 'general intelligence'; for test 1, as its name implies, is a test of comprehension. To obtain the loadings on these new axes or factors the original 10×2 matrix of loadings for factors I_0 and III_0 is post-multiplied by the orthogonal matrix

$$\begin{bmatrix} \cos\theta & \sin\theta \\ -\sin\theta & \cos\theta \end{bmatrix}.$$

The angle θ can be determined either by measurement from Figure 5·2(*a*) or by calculation. It is about 24° and the new loadings on factors I_1 and III_1 are given in Table 5·3(*a*).

Futher plots can now be made using the loadings on I_1, II_0 and III_1. That for factors II_0 and III_1, where subscripts refer to the number of rotations a factor has had, is given in Figure 5.2(*b*). Again it is clear that an orthogonal rotation of the axes, in an anticlockwise direction, can be performed which will eliminate virtually all negative loadings. (All can be eliminated by a further slight rotation of I_1 and II_1.) Here it is convenient to let the axis of factor II pass through test point 2, that is the Arithmetic test, as this may help in the interpretation of this new factor. The rotation matrix required now is:

$$\begin{bmatrix} \cos\phi & -\sin\phi \\ \sin\phi & \cos\phi \end{bmatrix}.$$

The angle ϕ in the figure is about 46° and the new loadings

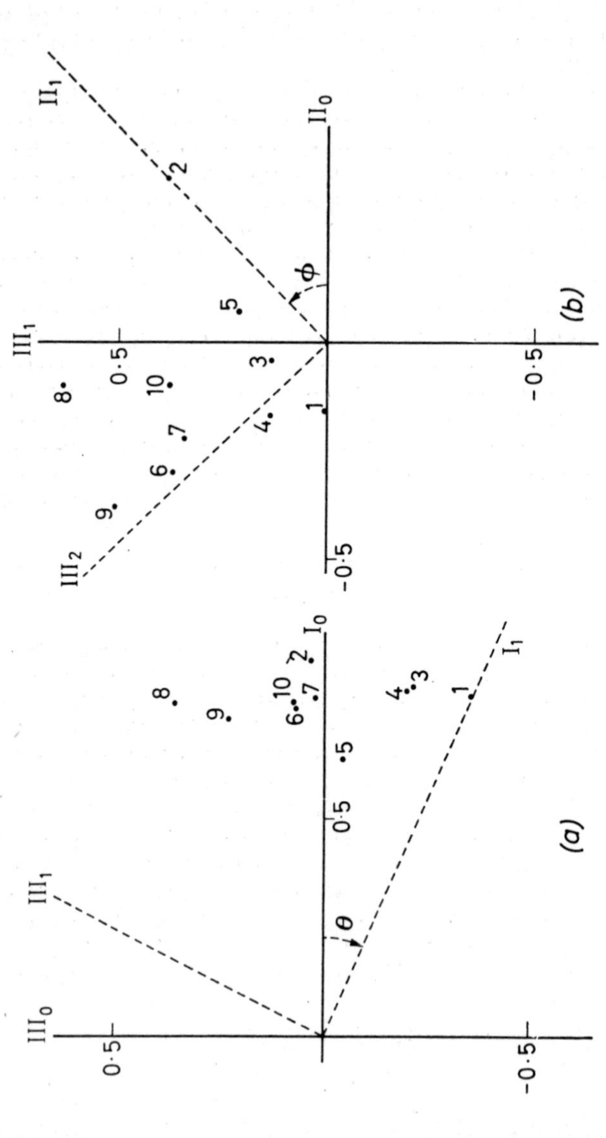

FIG. 5.2

on the factors, denoted by II_1 and III_2, together with the loadings on I_1, are given in Table 5.3(*b*). We have now almost eliminated all negative signs from the loadings, and in so doing have shown that the three orthogonal axes representing the factors can be so placed as to include all the test points in one octant of the factor space. However, we must hasten to add that other positions of the axes, different (though perhaps only slightly so) from those given here, would also have achieved this end.

Table 5.3. Loadings on rotated factors

Tests	(*a*)		(*b*)		
	I_1	III_1	I_1	II_1	III_2
1	0·863	0·000	0·863	−0·106	0·109
2	0·781	0·394	0·781	0·548	0·000
3	0·830	0·138	0·830	0·069	0·127
4	0·812	0·139	0·812	−0·018	0·219
5	0·602	0·223	0·602	0·209	0·105
6	0·662	0·369	0·662	0·058	0·471
7	0·703	0·345	0·703	0·094	0·399
8	0·554	0·640	0·554	0·397	0·510
9	0·576	0·508	0·576	0·098	0·629
10	0·675	0·379	0·675	0·202	0·336

Unhampered by the presence of negative signs we can now look at the new set of loadings (Table 5.3(*b*)) and see if the factors can be interpreted in a meaningful way. Factor I_1 can, with reasonable conviction, still be described as a factor of 'general intelligence'. On factor III_2 the largest loadings are for the last five tests of the set. The family resemblance between these tests, after the effect of factor I_1 has been removed, is thought to be concerned with the ability to visualize; so this third factor could tentatively be labelled 'visualization'. On factor II_1 the largest loadings are for Arithmetic and Block Design. Since the latter test is not concerned with numbers it would be unwise to think of the factor merely as one of numerical ability, and a better description of it might be 'mechanical knowledge', or even 'memory'.

The example just given illustrates a common type of approach to the problem of interpreting the results of factorial studies of an exploratory nature. Clearly the subjective element in it is large and, as a consequence, different investigators might interpret the same data differently. This possibility, however natural, is generally thought to be undesirable and to avoid it various empirical techniques for rotating factors, which in some predetermined sense would lead to a unique set of results, have been proposed (cf. Thurstone, 1954; Kaiser, 1958). We shall not consider them, but instead we shall describe other methods which seem promising and allow the investigator to test specific hypotheses about the factor content of his data without becoming involved in rotation techniques.

5.3. Methods of avoiding rotation

In pilot studies it is natural for an investigator to look at his results from different points of view and to see how they can best be summarized. In the process, too, as Eysenck (1953) and others have pointed out, factors suggesting hypotheses which had not previously occurred to the investigator may reveal themselves. After this preliminary work has been done he may be in a position to postulate in advance not only the number of factors to be expected in the analysis of further data but also where the zero, or near zero, loadings on them should occur. If the zero loadings are such as to determine the factors uniquely it is possible to obtain directly a set of approximate loadings which does not require rotation. Two ways of doing this will now be described, one for uncorrelated, the other for correlated factors (Lawley, 1960). Although the methods are approximate they are probably sufficiently accurate for most practical purposes. Should greater accuracy be desired, the results they give can be employed, as starting values, in iterative but efficient estimation procedures given in Chapter 6.

5.4. An approximate method for uncorrelated factors

The method for uncorrelated factors is to a certain extent arbitrary, since the values of the loadings will depend slightly on the order in which the factors are considered. The general principle is that the factors are ordered roughly according to the number of zero loadings they have, those with the highest number being considered first. For the method to work it is necessary that the rth factor in this order should have at least $k-r$ zero loadings, where k is the total number of common factors assumed to be present. The kth factor need have no zero loadings, and could thus correspond to a general factor.

By way of illustration we shall use the data from the example in Chapter 2 (although, for convenience here and in the next chapter where the same data are employed, variate *2* is omitted and the other variates are re-arranged in the order *5, 4, 6, 8, 9, 7, 1, 3*). The correlation matrix, with the variates renumbered from *1* to *8*, is given in Table 5.4. The size of the sample is 211.

We first guess or estimate the communalities. For our data the following estimates are available and will be employed:

1	*2*	*3*	*4*	*5*	*6*	*7*	*8*
0·638	0·782	0·843	0·440	0·757	0·619	0·561	0·368

Let $\mathbf{A}_0$ be the matrix formed from $\mathbf{A}$ (Table 5.4) by replacing the unities along the diagonal by the estimates of the communalities given above. The hypothesis with which we start the analysis is that there are three common factors, and that the required pattern of loadings (with x's representing those that are not necessarily zero) is as follows:

$$\begin{matrix} x & x & x & x & x & x & x & x \\ x & x & x & 0 & 0 & 0 & 0 & 0 \\ 0 & x & x & x & x & x & x & 0 \end{matrix}$$

In this chapter we shall suppose that the non-zero loadings denoted by x's are all positive, as is often the case in practice.

Corresponding to these three factors we write down a matrix $\mathbf{Q}'$, with three rows, by which $\mathbf{A}_0$ is to be pre-multiplied. The only essential condition which $\mathbf{Q}'$ must satisfy is that its rows should be linearly independent. The actual form of $\mathbf{Q}'$ will affect merely the efficiency of the estimation process. A simple general rule for choosing $\mathbf{Q}'$ is to put zeros for elements corresponding in position to zero loadings and unities elsewhere. (If, however, there were any suspected negative loadings, the corresponding elements of $\mathbf{Q}'$ would be taken as

Table 5.4. Correlation matrix A

1	*2*	*3*	*4*	*5*	*6*	*7*	*8*	*Row sums*
1·000	0·691	0·679	0·149	0·409	0·382	0·346	0·270	3·926
0·691	1·000	0·791	0·285	0·505	0·443	0·471	0·355	4·541
0·679	0·791	1·000	0·314	0·472	0·372	0·426	0·254	4·308
0·149	0·285	0·314	1·000	0·470	0·385	0·434	0·218	3·255
0·409	0·505	0·472	0·470	1·000	0·680	0·639	0·504	4·679
0·382	0·443	0·372	0·385	0·680	1·000	0·576	0·452	4·290
0·346	0·471	0·426	0·434	0·639	0·576	1·000	0·395	4·287
0·270	0·355	0·254	0·218	0·504	0·452	0·395	1·000	3·448

-1.) Thus in our example we shall take $\mathbf{Q}'$ to be

1	1	1	1	1	1	1	1
1	1	1	0	0	0	0	0
0	1	1	1	1	1	1	0

In certain cases this rule would have to be slightly modified, since, if strictly applied, it might give rows which were linearly dependent. Thus, for example, the first row might be merely the sum of the second and third rows. Simple modifications of the rule can, however, easily be devised to cope with the difficulty, for example some of the zeros may be replaced by unities, or *vice versa.*

The matrix $\mathbf{Q}'\mathbf{A}_0$, whose elements are merely sums or partial sums of the columns of $\mathbf{A}_0$, is easily found to be

3·564	4·323	4·151	2·695	4·436	3·909	3·848	2·816
2·008	2·264	2·313	0·748	1·386	1·197	1·243	0·879
2·656	3·277	3·218	2·328	3·523	3·075	3·107	2·178

We also calculate the matrix

$$\mathbf{H} = \mathbf{Q}'\mathbf{A}_0\mathbf{Q} = \begin{bmatrix} 29{\cdot}742 & 12{\cdot}038 & 23{\cdot}362 \\ 12{\cdot}038 & 6{\cdot}585 & 9{\cdot}151 \\ 23{\cdot}362 & 9{\cdot}151 & 18{\cdot}528 \end{bmatrix},$$

where $\mathbf{Q}$ is the transpose of $\mathbf{Q}'$. Usually, as here, $\mathbf{H}$ is positive definite. If it were not, some of the communalities would have to be increased.

The next stage of the process is to determine three row vectors $\mathbf{z}'_1$, $\mathbf{z}'_2$ and $\mathbf{z}'_3$ by which $\mathbf{Q}'\mathbf{A}_0$ is to be pre-multiplied. The elements of $\mathbf{z}'_r\mathbf{Q}'\mathbf{A}_0$ are to be proportional to the estimates of the loadings for the rth factor, and (for $r < k$) we shall choose $\mathbf{z}'_r$ such that certain of these elements are as small as possible. In order that the factors should be orthogonal $\mathbf{z}_1$, $\mathbf{z}_2$ and $\mathbf{z}_3$ must also satisfy the orthogonality relations

$$\mathbf{z}'_1\mathbf{H}\mathbf{z}_2 = \mathbf{z}'_2\mathbf{H}\mathbf{z}_3 = \mathbf{z}'_3\mathbf{H}\mathbf{z}_1 = 0.$$

In our example we start with the second factor, since this has the greatest number of zero loadings. We must choose $\mathbf{z}'_2$ so that the last five elements of $\mathbf{z}'_2\mathbf{Q}'\mathbf{A}_0$ are small. This could be done by trial and error; but we shall employ the method of least squares, and minimize the sum of squares of these elements. Let us write $\mathbf{z}'_2 = [x_2 \ 1 \ y_2]$. Then we choose x_2 and y_2 so as to minimize the expression

$$(2{\cdot}695x_2+0{\cdot}748+2{\cdot}328y_2)^2+\ldots+(2{\cdot}816x_2+0{\cdot}879+2{\cdot}178y_2)^2.$$

This leads to the 'normal' equations

$$64{\cdot}958x_2+52{\cdot}011y_2+20{\cdot}102 = 0,$$
$$52{\cdot}011x_2+41{\cdot}684y_2+16{\cdot}082 = 0.$$

Hence

$$\mathbf{z}'_2 = [-0{\cdot}5812 \quad 1{\cdot}0000 \quad 0{\cdot}3394]$$

and

$$\mathbf{z}'_2\mathbf{H} = [2{\cdot}6810 \quad 2{\cdot}6944 \quad 1{\cdot}8614].$$

Taking next the third factor, we choose $\mathbf{z}'_3 = [x_3 \ y_3 \ 1]$ in such a way that the sum of the squares of the first and last elements of $\mathbf{z}'_3\mathbf{Q}'\mathbf{A}_0$ is minimized with $\mathbf{z}_3$ satisfying $\mathbf{z}'_2\mathbf{H}\mathbf{z}_3 = 0$. Thus x_3 and y_3 must be chosen so as to minimize

$$\Sigma \equiv (3{\cdot}564x_3+2{\cdot}008y_3+2{\cdot}656)^2+(2{\cdot}816x_3+0{\cdot}879y_3+2{\cdot}178)^2$$

subject to the condition

$$\alpha \equiv 2{\cdot}6810x_3+2{\cdot}6944y_3+1{\cdot}8614 = 0.$$

To do this we form the equations

$$\frac{\partial\Sigma}{\partial x_3}+2\lambda\frac{\partial\alpha}{\partial x_3} = 0,$$

$$\frac{\partial\Sigma}{\partial y_3}+2\lambda\frac{\partial\alpha}{\partial y_3} = 0,$$

where 2λ is an indeterminate multiplier.

These equations are, numerically,

$$20{\cdot}632x_3+9{\cdot}632y_3+15{\cdot}599+2{\cdot}6810\lambda = 0,$$
$$9{\cdot}632x_3+4{\cdot}805y_3+7{\cdot}248+2{\cdot}6944\lambda = 0.$$

On eliminating λ we get

$$29{\cdot}795x_3+13{\cdot}066y_3+22{\cdot}592 = 0.$$

This equation, together with the equation $\alpha = 0$ above, enables us to solve for x_3 and y_3, and we find that $x_3 = -0{\cdot}8095$ and $y_3 = 0{\cdot}1148$.

Hence

$$\mathbf{z}'_3 = [-0\cdot8095 \quad 0\cdot1148 \quad 1\cdot0000]$$

and

$$\mathbf{z}'_3\mathbf{H} = [0\cdot6678 \quad 0\cdot1622 \quad 0\cdot6670].$$

Finally, $\mathbf{z}'_1 = [1 \; x_1 \; y_1]$ is determined by the conditions

$$\mathbf{z}'_2\mathbf{H}\mathbf{z}_1 = \mathbf{z}'_3\mathbf{H}\mathbf{z}_1 = 0,$$

i.e.

$$2\cdot6944x_1 + 1\cdot8614y_1 + 2\cdot6810 = 0,$$
$$0\cdot1622x_1 + 0\cdot6670y_1 + 0\cdot6678 = 0.$$

Thus

$$\mathbf{z}'_1 = [1\cdot0000 \quad -0\cdot3646 \quad -0\cdot9125]$$

and

$$\mathbf{z}'_1\mathbf{H} = [4\cdot0351 \quad 1\cdot2868 \quad 3\cdot1187].$$

We now calculate $\mathbf{z}'_1\mathbf{H}\mathbf{z}_1 = 0\cdot72012$, $\mathbf{z}'_2\mathbf{H}\mathbf{z}_2 = 1\cdot76796$, $\mathbf{z}'_3\mathbf{H}\mathbf{z}_3 = 0\cdot14505$ (which are positive as $\mathbf{H}$ is positive definite), and divide the vectors $\mathbf{z}'_1$, $\mathbf{z}'_2$, $\mathbf{z}'_3$ respectively by the square roots of these values to obtain standardized vectors $\mathbf{w}'_1$, $\mathbf{w}'_2$ and $\mathbf{w}'_3$. This standardization is necessary in order that the factors should have unit variances. We find that

$$\mathbf{w}'_1 = [1\cdot1784 \quad -0\cdot4296 \quad -1\cdot0753],$$
$$\mathbf{w}'_2 = [-0\cdot4371 \quad 0\cdot7521 \quad 0\cdot2553],$$
$$\mathbf{w}'_3 = [-2\cdot1256 \quad 0\cdot3014 \quad 2\cdot6258].$$

Pre-multiplication of $\mathbf{Q}'\mathbf{A}_0$ successively by $\mathbf{w}'_1$, $\mathbf{w}'_2$ and $\mathbf{w}'_3$ gives the estimated loadings for the three factors. The matrix $\mathbf{L}'$ of loadings is as follows:

0·481	0·598	0·438	0·351	0·844	0·786	0·660	0·599
0·630	0·650	0·747	(−0·021)	(0·003)	(−0·023)	(0·046)	(−0·014)
(0·004)	0·098	0·324	0·610	0·239	0·126	0·354	(−0·002)

The above values are, on the whole, not very different from the maximum likelihood estimates given in the next chapter (page 78). Those in brackets are satisfactorily small and can be replaced by zeros.

If a further iteration of the process were contemplated new estimates of the communalities could be found in the usual way.

5.5. An approximate method for correlated factors

With correlated factors the process of estimation is similar. Now, however, the order in which the factors are considered is irrelevant. A necessary (though not sufficient) condition for the factors to be determined uniquely is that each must have at least $k-1$ zero loadings. The vectors $\mathbf{z}'_r$ no longer have to satisfy orthogonality conditions, but instead it is necessary to estimate the correlation coefficients between the factors. To ensure uniqueness in our numerical example we must make an alteration in the hypothesis regarding the factors. The pattern of loadings is the same as before except that the third and fourth x's in the first row are replaced by zeros. The matrix $\mathbf{Q}'$ is now taken as:

$$\begin{matrix} 1 & 1 & 0 & 0 & 1 & 1 & 1 & 1 \\ 1 & 1 & 1 & 0 & 0 & 0 & 0 & 0 \\ 0 & 1 & 1 & 1 & 1 & 1 & 1 & 0 \end{matrix}$$

Hence $\mathbf{Q}'\mathbf{A}_0$ is as follows:

2·736	3·247	2·994	1·941	3·494	3·152	2·988	2·344
2·008	2·264	2·313	0·748	1·386	1·197	1·243	0·879
2·656	3·277	3·218	2·328	3·523	3·075	3·107	2·178

We also find

$$\mathbf{H} = \mathbf{Q}'\mathbf{A}_0\mathbf{Q} = \begin{bmatrix} 17·961 & 8·977 & 17·816 \\ 8·977 & 6·585 & 9·151 \\ 17·816 & 9·151 & 18·528 \end{bmatrix},$$

which satisfies the necessary condition of being positive definite. In this case we can choose the vector $\mathbf{z}'_1 = [1 \;\; x_1 \;\; y_1]$ so that the loadings of the third and fourth variates in the first factor are exactly zero. The equations for x_1 and x_2 are

$$2·313x_1 + 3·218y_1 + 2·994 = 0,$$
$$0·748x_1 + 2·328y_1 + 1·941 = 0.$$

Hence

$$\mathbf{z}'_1 = [1·0000 \quad -0·2431 \quad -0·7556].$$

Similarly we can choose $\mathbf{z}'_3 = [x_3 \;\; y_3 \;\; 1]$ so that the loadings of the first and last variates for the third factor are exactly zero. The equations for x_3 and y_3 are

$$2{\cdot}736x_3+2{\cdot}008y_3+2{\cdot}656 = 0,$$

$$2{\cdot}344x_3+0{\cdot}879y_3+2{\cdot}178 = 0;$$

and thus

$$\mathbf{z}'_3 = [-0{\cdot}8857 \quad -0{\cdot}1159 \quad 1{\cdot}0000].$$

For the second factor we choose $\mathbf{z}'_2 = [x_2 \; 1 \; y_2]$ in such a way that the sum of squares of the last five elements of $\mathbf{z}'_2\mathbf{Q}'\mathbf{A}_0$ is a minimum. The normal equations for x_2 and y_2 are

$$40{\cdot}333x_2+40{\cdot}909y_2+15{\cdot}842 = 0,$$

$$40{\cdot}909x_2+41{\cdot}684y_2+16{\cdot}082 = 0,$$

giving

$$\mathbf{z}'_2 = [-0{\cdot}3196 \quad 1{\cdot}0000 \quad -0{\cdot}0721].$$

Let $\mathbf{Z}'$ be the matrix whose three rows are, in order, $\mathbf{z}'_1$, $\mathbf{z}'_2$ and $\mathbf{z}'_3$. Then, finding $\mathbf{Z}'\mathbf{HZ}$ and its inverse, we have

$$\mathbf{Z}'\mathbf{HZ} = \begin{bmatrix} 1{\cdot}0020 & -0{\cdot}3936 & -0{\cdot}5140 \\ -0{\cdot}3936 & 2{\cdot}2794 & 0{\cdot}0380 \\ -0{\cdot}5140 & 0{\cdot}0380 & 0{\cdot}8688 \end{bmatrix},$$

$$(\mathbf{Z}'\mathbf{HZ})^{-1} = \begin{bmatrix} 1{\cdot}5688 & 0{\cdot}2556 & 0{\cdot}9169 \\ 0{\cdot}2556 & 0{\cdot}4807 & 0{\cdot}1302 \\ 0{\cdot}9169 & 0{\cdot}1302 & 1{\cdot}6878 \end{bmatrix}.$$

We put the latter matrix in the form $\mathbf{DPD}$, where $\mathbf{D}$ is a diagonal matrix with elements $(1{\cdot}2525 \quad 0{\cdot}6933 \quad 1{\cdot}2992)$, and where

$$\mathbf{P} = \begin{bmatrix} 1{\cdot}000 & 0{\cdot}294 & 0{\cdot}563 \\ 0{\cdot}294 & 1{\cdot}000 & 0{\cdot}145 \\ 0{\cdot}563 & 0{\cdot}145 & 1{\cdot}000 \end{bmatrix}.$$

The non-diagonal elements of $\mathbf{P}$ represent estimates of the factor correlation coefficients.

In order to obtain loadings for factors with unit variances we find

$$\mathbf{W}' = \mathbf{DZ}' = \begin{bmatrix} 1{\cdot}2525 & -0{\cdot}3045 & -0{\cdot}9464 \\ -0{\cdot}2216 & 0{\cdot}6933 & -0{\cdot}0500 \\ -1{\cdot}1507 & -0{\cdot}1506 & 1{\cdot}2992 \end{bmatrix}.$$

Pre-multiplication of $\mathbf{Q}'\mathbf{A}_0$ by $\mathbf{W}'$ then gives the matrix $\mathbf{L}'$ of loadings as follows:

0·302	0·276	0	0	0·620	0·673	0·424	0·607
0·653	0·686	0·779	(−0·028)	(0·010)	(−0·022)	(0·044)	(−0·019)
0	0·180	0·387	0·678	0·348	0·188	0·411	0

The values obtained are again not very different from the maximum likelihood estimates given in the next chapter. As before we may replace the bracketed elements by zeros.

The diagonal elements of the matrix $\mathbf{A}-\mathbf{LPL}'$ provide estimates of the residual variances and constitute the diagonal matrix $\mathbf{V}$. They are as follows:

0·3664 0·2178 0·1560 0·5403 0·2516 0·3693 0·4551 0·6316

5.6. Tests of significance

For the methods described in the last two sections the approximate χ^2 test given at the end of Chapter 3 may be used to test the significance of the residuals, subject to the cautionary remarks which accompanied it. The calculations are the same whether the factors are correlated or uncorrelated and are exactly as described in Section 3.6.

For the numerical data used in Sections 5.4 and 5.5 we have $n = 210$, $p = 8$, $k = 3$, and the number of degrees of freedom for χ^2 is 7. In the case of uncorrelated factors the value of χ^2 is found to be 4·2, while for correlated factors it is 3·7. In either case it is well below expectation, so that in spite of the rather small number of degrees of freedom it seems reasonable to accept the hypothesis which has been set up.

Exercises

1. Make the hypothesis that the correlations in Table 3.1 can be accounted for by two correlated factors and that the

pattern of loadings is as follows:

	Variates					
	1	*2*	*3*	*4*	*5*	*6*
1st factor	x	x	x	0	0	0
2nd factor	0	0	0	x	x	x

Using the estimates of the communalities given in Table 3.6, show by the method of Section 5.5 that the estimates of the loadings are:

0·662	0·561	0·702	(−0·029)	(−0·001)	(0·035)
(0·015)	(0·137)	(−0·160)	0·781	0·762	0·626

Show also that the estimate of the correlation coefficient between the factors is 0·578.

2. In the following matrix the first three variates are measures of 'rigidity' and the last three are measures of 'neuroticism':

1·000	0·638	0·704	0·150	0·160	0·228
0·638	1·000	0·570	0·245	0·196	0·269
0·704	0·570	1·000	0·081	0·007	0·172
0·150	0·245	0·081	1·000	0·363	0·533
0·160	0·196	0·007	0·363	1·000	0·447
0·228	0·269	0·172	0·533	0·447	1·000

If the pattern of loadings on two uncorrelated factors is taken to be

x	x	x	x	x	x
x	x	x	0	0	0

and the highest loading in each column of the matrix is taken as an estimate of the communality for the test concerned, show, using the methods of Section 5.4 that the estimates of the loadings are as follows:

0·274	0·356	0·138	0·697	0·613	0·739
0·799	0·684	0·814	(0·026)	(0·047)	(−0·044)

REFERENCES

Cattell, R. B. (1952), *Factor Analysis*, Harper and Bros, New York

Eysenck, H. J. (1953), The logical basis of factor analysis, *The Amer. Psychologist*, **8**, 105–114

Kaiser, H. F. (1958), The varimax criterion for analytical rotation in factor analysis, *Psychometrika* **23**, 187–200

Lawley, D. N. (1955), A statistical examination of the centroid method, *Proc. Roy. Soc. Edin.* **A64**, 175–189

Lawley, D. N. (1960), Approximate methods in factor analysis, *Brit. J. Statist. Psychol.* **13**, 11–17

Thurstone, L. L. (1947), *Multiple Factor Analysis*, University of Chicago Press

Thurstone, L. L. (1954), An analytical method of simple structure, *Psychometrika* **19**, 173–182

6

ESTIMATION OF FACTOR LOADINGS UNDER VARIOUS INITIAL ASSUMPTIONS

6.1. Introduction

In Sections 5.4 and 5.5 of the last chapter approximate methods were given for estimating a set of loadings when the positions of those that are zero can be postulated in advance. In this chapter efficient methods of doing this are described. The problems that arise were first discussed by Anderson and Rubin (1955) and by Howe (1955), but the treatment here is that given by one of the authors (Lawley, 1958). Sections dealing with the estimation problem when the factors are (*a*) uncorrelated and (*b*) correlated are followed by one in which tests of significance of the residual matrices are derived. It is assumed that before the analysis begins the investigator has already obtained approximate estimates of the loadings either by use of the methods described in the last chapter or from an earlier analysis of similar data.

6.2. Equations of estimation for uncorrelated factors

The basic factor model and the notation are the same as in Chapter 2, but, as was remarked above, certain of the l_{ir} are now assumed *a priori* to be zero. These will be referred to simply as 'zero loadings'.

Maximum likelihood estimates are again obtained by maximizing expression (2.3) with respect to the unknown parameters. As before $\partial L/\partial l_{ir}$ is $-n$ times the element in the rth row and ith column of $\mathbf{L}'\mathbf{C}^{-1}-\mathbf{L}'\mathbf{C}^{-1}\mathbf{A}\mathbf{C}^{-1}$, but in the present instance the elements are equated to zero only for i and r such that l_{ir} is a 'non-zero' loading. This may be expressed by the statement that those elements of the matrix

$$\mathbf{Q}' = \hat{\mathbf{L}}'\hat{\mathbf{C}}^{-1}-\hat{\mathbf{L}}'\hat{\mathbf{C}}^{-1}\mathbf{A}\hat{\mathbf{C}}^{-1} \tag{6.1}$$

which correspond in position to the non-zero elements of $\mathbf{L}'$ (and of $\hat{\mathbf{L}}'$) are to be equated to zero.

As in Chapter 2, $\partial L/\partial v_i$ is $-\frac{1}{2}n$ times the ith diagonal element of the matrix $\mathbf{C}^{-1}-\mathbf{C}^{-1}\mathbf{A}\mathbf{C}^{-1}$. Hence the second set of equations of estimation is the same as before, and we have

$$\operatorname{diag}(\hat{\mathbf{C}}^{-1}-\hat{\mathbf{C}}^{-1}\mathbf{A}\hat{\mathbf{C}}^{-1}) = 0. \tag{6.2}$$

These equations are not in forms which are suitable for practical solution, but they may be transformed to make them so. It will be convenient at this point to discard all circumflex accents. By **L**, **V** and **C** we shall in future mean $\hat{\mathbf{L}}$, $\hat{\mathbf{V}}$ and $\hat{\mathbf{C}}$. If we post-multiply by **V** in (6.1) and remember that $\mathbf{V} = \mathbf{C}-\mathbf{LL}'$, we obtain

$$\mathbf{Q}'\mathbf{V} = \mathbf{L}'-\mathbf{L}'\mathbf{C}^{-1}\mathbf{A}-\mathbf{KL}', \tag{6.3}$$

where $\mathbf{K} = [k_{rs}]$ is a symmetric matrix of order k given by

$$\mathbf{K} = \mathbf{L}'\mathbf{C}^{-1}(\mathbf{C}-\mathbf{A})\mathbf{C}^{-1}\mathbf{L} = \mathbf{Q}'\mathbf{L}. \tag{6.4}$$

Since **V** is diagonal, $\mathbf{Q}'\mathbf{V}$ has zeros in the same positions as $\mathbf{Q}'$. It may also be observed that, in view of the properties of $\mathbf{Q}'$, the diagonal elements of **K** must be zero. The non-diagonal elements of **K** are not, however, necessarily zero; on this more will be said later.

To simplify (6.2) we first post-multiply the matrix on the left-hand side by **V**, in the form $\mathbf{C}-\mathbf{LL}'$. The diagonal elements are still zero and, in view of the fact that $\operatorname{diag}(\mathbf{QL}') = 0$, we find that

$$\operatorname{diag}(\mathbf{I}-\mathbf{C}^{-1}\mathbf{A}) = 0,$$

where **I** denotes the unit matrix, in this case of order p. Pre-multiplication by **V** then yields the equation

$$\mathbf{V} = \operatorname{diag}(\mathbf{A}-\mathbf{LL}'\mathbf{C}^{-1}\mathbf{A}). \tag{6.5}$$

Except in particular cases this does not lead to the usual estimates for the residual variances; and the diagonal elements of **C** are not, in general, equal to the corresponding elements of **A**. Equations (6.3) and (6.5), though expressed in different notation, are the same as those reached by Howe, and the following discussion of their practical solution has much in common with his, though some points are here given greater emphasis.

As an example let us consider seven variates depending on three common factors. Using x's to denote the non-zero loadings, let us suppose that the pattern of these is assumed to be as follows:

$$\begin{matrix} x & x & x & x & x & x & x \\ x & x & x & x & x & 0 & 0 \\ 0 & 0 & 0 & x & x & x & x \end{matrix}$$

It will be noticed that the variates in which the second factor has non-zero loadings form a sub-set of those in which the first factor has non-zero loadings. A brief examination of the positions of the zeros in **L** and **Q** is sufficient to show that, as a consequence, $k_{12} = k_{21} = 0$. Similar considerations apply to the first and third factors, and so also $k_{13} = k_{31} = 0$. When, however, the second and third factors are paired, the set of variates in which either factor has non-zero loadings is not a sub-set of those in which the other factor has non-zero loadings. Hence $k_{23} = k_{32}$ is not necessarily zero. This is the only non-zero element of **K**.

Now denote the three rows of $\mathbf{L}'$, in order, by $\mathbf{l}'_1$, $\mathbf{l}'_2$ and $\mathbf{l}'_3$. Then, in this example, (6.3) implies that the non-zero elements of $\mathbf{l}'_1$, $\mathbf{l}'_2$ and $\mathbf{l}'_3$ are equal to the corresponding elements of the row vectors $\mathbf{u}'_1$, $\mathbf{u}'_2$ and $\mathbf{u}'_3$, respectively, where

$$\begin{aligned} \mathbf{u}'_1 &= \mathbf{l}'_1\mathbf{C}^{-1}\mathbf{A}, \\ \mathbf{u}'_2 &= \mathbf{l}'_2\mathbf{C}^{-1}\mathbf{A}+k_{23}\mathbf{l}'_3, \\ \mathbf{u}'_3 &= \mathbf{l}'_3\mathbf{C}^{-1}\mathbf{A}+k_{23}\mathbf{l}'_2. \end{aligned}$$

This, as will be seen, leads to an iterative method for solving the equations of estimation. For purposes of computation we note that, as in Chapter 2, the inverse of **C** is given by

$$\mathbf{C}^{-1} = \mathbf{V}^{-1}-\mathbf{V}^{-1}\mathbf{L}(\mathbf{I}+\mathbf{J})^{-1}\mathbf{L}'\mathbf{V}^{-1},$$

and that

$$\mathbf{L}'\mathbf{C}^{-1} = (\mathbf{I}+\mathbf{J})^{-1}\mathbf{L}'\mathbf{V}^{-1},$$

where $\mathbf{J} = \mathbf{L}'\mathbf{V}^{-1}\mathbf{L}$. The calculations required are more tedious than those that occur in the ordinary maximum likelihood method since in each iteration the inversion of the kth order matrix $\mathbf{I}+\mathbf{J}$ is necessary, and this is not in general diagonal.

Suppose instead that the pattern of loadings were as shown below:

$$\begin{matrix} x & x & x & x & x & x & x \\ x & x & x & x & 0 & 0 & 0 \\ 0 & 0 & 0 & 0 & x & x & x \end{matrix}$$

As before, k_{23} is the only non-zero element of **K**, but now contributions arising from k_{23} may be ignored. The reason is that there is no 'overlap' between the loadings for the second and third factors, i.e. there are no variates in which both factors have non-zero loadings. In this case the non-zero elements of $\mathbf{L}'$ are equal to the corresponding elements of $\mathbf{L}'\mathbf{C}^{-1}\mathbf{A}$.

Thus for certain patterns of loadings the equations arising from (6.3) can be simplified by omitting the term in **K**, in which case (6.5) can be simplified to $\mathbf{V} = \text{diag}\,(\mathbf{A} - \mathbf{LL}')$, giving the usual estimates of the residual variances. For such cases Howe recommends a Gauss–Seidel type of iterative technique which will not, however, be described here. The method is very laborious, but he claims that it gives more rapid convergence than other methods. It may be noted that for both the patterns given above the loadings are uniquely determined, since in either case any orthogonal rotation of the factors would destroy the arrangement of zeros.

6.3. Iterative method for uncorrelated factors

In the numerical example which will be used to illustrate the method of solving the equations there are eight variates, assumed to depend on three factors, and the pattern of loadings was assumed to be as follows:

$$\begin{matrix} x & x & x & x & x & x & x & x \\ x & x & x & 0 & 0 & 0 & 0 & 0 \\ 0 & x & x & x & x & x & x & 0 \end{matrix}$$

It must be made clear that this is not really an *a priori* hypothesis, since it was derived from a previous analysis of the data; so we are not in fact justified in using the same data to test the hypothesis. The example is chosen merely to exhibit the type of calculation required, and we shall proceed as if the hypothesis had been made *a priori*.

Suppose that $\mathbf{L}_{(1)}$, $\mathbf{V}_{(1)}$ and $\mathbf{C}_{(1)} = \mathbf{L}_{(1)}\mathbf{L}'_{(1)} + \mathbf{V}_{(1)}$ are approximations to **L**, **V** and **C**. By an iterative procedure we are able to obtain better approximations, $\mathbf{L}_{(2)}$, $\mathbf{V}_{(2)}$ and $\mathbf{C}_{(2)}$. We calculate first $\mathbf{L}'_{(1)}\mathbf{V}_{(1)}^{-1}$ and $\mathbf{J}_{(1)} = \mathbf{L}'_{(1)}\mathbf{V}_{(1)}^{-1}\mathbf{L}_{(1)}$, then $(\mathbf{I}+\mathbf{J}_{(1)})^{-1}$ and $\mathbf{L}'_{(1)}\mathbf{V}_{(1)}^{-1}\mathbf{A}$. Hence we find

$$\begin{aligned} \mathbf{M}'_{(1)} &= \mathbf{L}'_{(1)}\mathbf{C}_{(1)}^{-1}\mathbf{A} \\ &= (\mathbf{I}+\mathbf{J}_{(1)})^{-1}\mathbf{L}'_{(1)}\mathbf{V}_{(1)}^{-1}\mathbf{A}. \end{aligned}$$

An approximation to **K** is then given by

$$\mathbf{K}_{(1)} = \mathbf{L}'_{(1)}\mathbf{C}_{(1)}{}^{-1}(\mathbf{C}_{(1)}-\mathbf{A})\mathbf{C}_{(1)}{}^{-1}\mathbf{L}_{(1)},$$

which is calculated in the form

$$\mathbf{K}_{(1)} = (\mathbf{L}'_{(1)}-\mathbf{M}'_{(1)})(\mathbf{V}_{(1)}{}^{-1}\mathbf{L}_{(1)})(\mathbf{I}+\mathbf{J}_{(1)})^{-1}.$$

The complete matrix $\mathbf{K}_{(1)}$ is not of immediate interest; we require, however, an estimate $k_{23}{}^{(1)}$ of k_{23}, the only non-zero element of **K** in this case. Let us denote the three rows of $\mathbf{L}'_{(1)}$, in order, by $\mathbf{l}'_{1(1)}$, $\mathbf{l}'_{2(1)}$ and $\mathbf{l}'_{3(1)}$, and those of $\mathbf{M}'_{(1)}$ similarly. Then the non-zero elements of $\mathbf{L}'_{(2)}$, our next approximation to $\mathbf{L}'$, are the corresponding elements of the three row vectors

$$\mathbf{m}'_{1(1)},$$
$$\mathbf{m}'_{2(1)}+k_{23}{}^{(1)}\mathbf{l}'_{3(1)},$$
$$\mathbf{m}'_{3(1)}+k_{23}{}^{(1)}\mathbf{l}'_{2(1)}.$$

Finally, the next approximation to **V** is given by

$$\mathbf{V}_{(2)} = \text{diag}(\mathbf{A}-\mathbf{L}_{(2)}\mathbf{M}'_{(1)}).$$

This method appears to converge. A slightly different procedure is adopted by Howe, which may hasten convergence to some extent, but we shall not discuss it here.

6.4. Numerical example

The data used for the calculations are those given in Table 5.4. The initial trial values for **L** and **V** were derived from rotated loadings given by Emmett (1949), and a number of iterations were performed on a desk machine. The last of these is reproduced below, with $\mathbf{L}'_{(1)}$ and $\mathbf{V}_{(1)}$ representing values obtained from the preceding iteration:

$\mathbf{L}_{(1)}$	0·500	0·563	0·439	0·358	0·807	0·765	0·663	0·607
	0·623	0·659	0·738	0	0	0	0	0
	0	0·179	0·328	0·558	0·325	0·183	0·349	0
$\mathbf{V}_{(1)}$	0·3619	0·2177	0·1570	0·5605	0·2431	0·3813	0·4386	0·6316
$\mathbf{L}'_{(1)}\mathbf{V}_{(1)}{}^{-1}$	1·382	2·586	2·796	0·639	3·320	2·006	1·512	0·961
	1·721	3·027	4·701	0	0	0	0	0
	0	0·822	2·089	0·996	1·337	0·480	0·796	0

$$\mathbf{J}_{(1)} = \begin{bmatrix} 9{\cdot}4023 & 4{\cdot}6286 & 3{\cdot}7100 \\ 4{\cdot}6286 & 6{\cdot}5364 & 2{\cdot}0836 \\ 3{\cdot}7100 & 2{\cdot}0836 & 2{\cdot}1879 \end{bmatrix}$$

$$(\mathbf{I}+\mathbf{J}_{(1)})^{-1} = \begin{bmatrix} 0{\cdot}18874 & -0{\cdot}06737 & -0{\cdot}17563 \\ -0{\cdot}06737 & 0{\cdot}18600 & -0{\cdot}04317 \\ -0{\cdot}17563 & -0{\cdot}04317 & 0{\cdot}54629 \end{bmatrix}$$

									Row sums
$\mathbf{L}'_{(1)}\mathbf{V}_{(1)}^{-1}\mathbf{A}$	8·069	9·553	9·182	5·658	9·626	8·529	8·333	6·279	65·229
	7·005	7·935	8·264	2·595	4·451	3·747	4·024	2·733	40·754
	3·140	4·021	4·201	3·045	4·041	3·372	3·636	2·245	27·701

									Row sums
$\mathbf{M}'_{(1)}$	0·4995	0·5622	0·4384	0·3583	0·8072	0·7651	0·6631	0·6067	4·7005
	0·6238	0·6587	0·7372	−0·0300	0·0049	−0·0232	0·0301	−0·0116	1·9899
	−0·0042	0·1763	0·3256	0·5577	0·3248	0·1824	0·3491	0·0057	1·9174

$$\mathbf{K}_{(1)} = 10^{-4}\begin{bmatrix} 0 & 8 & -2 \\ 8 & -11 & 36 \\ -2 & 36 & 4 \end{bmatrix} \qquad k_{23}{}^{(1)} = 0{\cdot}0036$$

$\mathbf{L}'_{(2)}$	0·4995	0·5622	0·4384	0·3583	0·8072	0·7651	0·6631	0·6067
	0·6238	0·6593	0·7384	0	0	0	0	0
	0	0·1787	0·3283	0·5577	0·3248	0·1824	0·3491	0
$\mathbf{V}_{(2)}$	0·3614	0·2181	0·1566	0·5606	0·2429	0·3814	0·4384	0·6319

To save space we have written $\mathbf{V}_{(1)}$ and $\mathbf{V}_{(2)}$ as above, though they are really diagonal. The convergence, as in many cases, is extremely slow. At this stage a programme for doing the calculations on the Mercury Computer was written (Nixon, Gallagher and Maxwell, 1962), and further iterations were carried out. The loadings, after about fifty iterations, converged to the following values:

0·499	0·562	0·437	0·364	0·809	0·767	0·665	0·605
0·625	0·658	0·740	0	0	0	0	0
0	0·179	0·336	0·547	0·321	0·175	0·345	0

Although these differ somewhat from those given above, the differences are only in the third decimal places and do not noticeably affect the fit. The effect of k_{23} is not very large, its final value being $4{\cdot}83 \times 10^{-3}$.

6.5. Equations of estimation for correlated factors

Now suppose that the factors are correlated. Let **P** be their correlation matrix, of order k. Each diagonal element of **P** is unity and the element in the rth row and the sth column is ρ_{rs}, the correlation between the rth and sth factors. We assume, as before, that the variance of each factor is unity.

With the same meaning as before for **C**, **L** and **V**, the log-likelihood function is again given by (2.3). But the elements of **C** are now:

$$c_{ii} = \sum_{r,s} l_{ir} l_{is} \rho_{rs} + v_i \quad (\text{where } \rho_{rr} = 1),$$

$$c_{ij} = \sum_{r,s} l_{ir} l_{js} \rho_{rs} \quad (i \neq j),$$

which in matrix notation is $\mathbf{C} = \mathbf{LPL}' + \mathbf{V}$.

We must now maximize (2.3) not only with respect to the non-zero l_{ir} and to the v_i, but also with respect to the factor correlation coefficients ρ_{rs}. This leads to three sets of equations.

Proceeding as in Chapter 2, we find that now $\partial L/\partial l_{ir}$ is $-n$ times the element in the rth row and ith column of

$$\mathbf{P}(\mathbf{L}'\mathbf{C}^{-1} - \mathbf{L}'\mathbf{C}^{-1}\mathbf{A}\mathbf{C}^{-1}).$$

Using circumflex accents to denote estimated values, the first set of equations is obtained by equating to zero those elements of the matrix

$$\mathbf{Q}' = \hat{\mathbf{P}}(\hat{\mathbf{L}}'\hat{\mathbf{C}}^{-1} - \hat{\mathbf{L}}'\hat{\mathbf{C}}^{-1}\mathbf{A}\hat{\mathbf{C}}^{-1}) \tag{6.6}$$

which correspond in position to the non-zero elements of $\mathbf{L}'$.

The second set of equations is

$$\operatorname{diag}(\hat{\mathbf{C}}^{-1} - \hat{\mathbf{C}}^{-1}\mathbf{A}\hat{\mathbf{C}}^{-1}) = 0, \tag{6.7}$$

as in the orthogonal case. In addition we now have to equate to zero, for $r \neq s$, the partial derivatives of L with respect to the ρ_{rs}. It is found that $\partial L/\partial \rho_{rs}$ is $-n$ times the element in the rth row and sth column of the matrix

$$\mathbf{K} = \mathbf{L}'\mathbf{C}^{-1}(\mathbf{C} - \mathbf{A})\mathbf{C}^{-1}\mathbf{L}, \tag{6.8}$$

and thus **K** is a diagonal matrix.

These equations may be simplified in much the same manner as those for the orthogonal case. For convenience we again drop circumflex accents. We first post-multiply (6.6) by $\mathbf{L}$ and obtain $\mathbf{Q}'\mathbf{L} = \mathbf{PK}$. This matrix must have zero diagonal elements, in view of the properties of $\mathbf{Q}'$. But the non-diagonal elements of $\mathbf{K}$ are zero, and therefore so also must be its diagonal elements. Thus $\mathbf{K} = 0$.

Let us next post-multiply (6.6) by $\mathbf{V}$, remembering that $\mathbf{V} = \mathbf{C}-\mathbf{LPL}'$ and that $\mathbf{K} = 0$. We then obtain

$$\mathbf{Q}'\mathbf{V} = \mathbf{P}(\mathbf{L}'-\mathbf{L}'\mathbf{C}^{-1}\mathbf{A}), \tag{6.9}$$

a matrix which has zeros in the same positions as $\mathbf{Q}'$.

Now post-multiply the left-hand side of (6.7) by $\mathbf{V}$, in the form $\mathbf{C}-\mathbf{LPL}'$, and use the fact that $\operatorname{diag}(\mathbf{QL}')= 0$. The result still has zero diagonal elements, and so

$$\operatorname{diag}(\mathbf{I}-\mathbf{C}^{-1}\mathbf{A}) = 0.$$

Pre-multiplication by $\mathbf{V}$ then gives

$$\operatorname{diag}(\mathbf{V}-\mathbf{A}-\mathbf{LPL}'\mathbf{C}^{-1}\mathbf{A}) = 0,$$

which, by use of (6.9) and of the fact that $\operatorname{diag}(\mathbf{LQ}'\mathbf{V}) = 0$ is easily seen to be equivalent to

$$\mathbf{V} = \operatorname{diag}(\mathbf{A}-\mathbf{LPL}'). \tag{6.10}$$

This means that the diagonal elements of $\mathbf{C}$ are equal to the corresponding elements of $\mathbf{A}$.

For purposes of computation we may note that the inverse of $\mathbf{C}$ is now given by

$$\mathbf{C}^{-1} = \mathbf{V}^{-1}-\mathbf{V}^{-1}\mathbf{L}(\mathbf{P}^{-1}+\mathbf{J})^{-1}\mathbf{L}'\mathbf{V}^{-1},$$

with $\mathbf{J}$ as before, and that

$$\mathbf{L}'\mathbf{C}^{-1} = (\mathbf{I}+\mathbf{JP})^{-1}\mathbf{L}'\mathbf{V}^{-1}.$$

Using this result, the equation $\mathbf{K} = 0$, may be put in the form

$$\mathbf{P} = \mathbf{J}^{-1}(\mathbf{L}'\mathbf{V}^{-1}\mathbf{A}\mathbf{V}^{-1}\mathbf{L})\mathbf{J}^{-1}-\mathbf{J}^{-1}. \tag{6.11}$$

These equations, in different notation, were previously given by Anderson and Rubin and independently by Howe. Our derivation is rather more condensed. Eqs (6.9), (6.10) and (6.11) can be solved by an iterative method, which at each stage requires the calculation of $\mathbf{J}^{-1}$ and of $(\mathbf{P}^{-1}+\mathbf{J})^{-1}$. If $k > 3$, a feasible method of doing this is to find

$$\mathbf{Z} = (\mathbf{J}+\mathbf{JPJ})^{-1}.$$

The two matrices required are then given by

$$(\mathbf{P}^{-1}+\mathbf{J})^{-1} = \mathbf{Z}(\mathbf{JP}),$$
$$\mathbf{J}^{-1} = \mathbf{Z}(\mathbf{I}+\mathbf{JP}) = \mathbf{Z}+\mathbf{Z}(\mathbf{JP}).$$

6.6. Iterative method for correlated factors

Let $\mathbf{L}_{(1)}$, $\mathbf{V}_{(1)}$ and $\mathbf{P}_{(1)}$ be approximations to $\mathbf{L}$, $\mathbf{V}$ and $\mathbf{P}$, so that

$$\mathbf{C}_{(1)} = \mathbf{L}_{(1)}\mathbf{P}_{(1)}\mathbf{L}'_{(1)}+\mathbf{V}_{(1)}$$

is an approximation to $\mathbf{C}$. We first calculate $\mathbf{L}'_{(1)}\mathbf{V}_{(1)}{}^{-1}$ and $\mathbf{J}_{(1)} = \mathbf{L}'_{(1)}\mathbf{V}_{(1)}{}^{-1}\mathbf{L}_{(1)}$, then $\mathbf{J}_{(1)}{}^{-1}$ and $(\mathbf{P}_{(1)}{}^{-1}+\mathbf{J}_{(1)})^{-1}$. After that we find $\mathbf{L}'_{(1)}\mathbf{V}_{(1)}{}^{-1}\mathbf{A}$ and hence

$$\begin{aligned}\mathbf{M}'_{(1)} &= \mathbf{P}_{(1)}\mathbf{L}'_{(1)}\mathbf{C}_{(1)}{}^{-1}\mathbf{A}\\ &= (\mathbf{P}_{(1)}{}^{-1}+\mathbf{J}_{(1)})^{-1}\mathbf{L}'_{(1)}\mathbf{V}_{(1)}{}^{-1}\mathbf{A}.\end{aligned}$$

The elements of $\mathbf{L}'_{(2)}$, our next approximation to $\mathbf{L}'$, are obtained by equating those elements of $\mathbf{P}_{(1)}\mathbf{L}'_{(2)}$ which correspond in position to non-zero elements of $\mathbf{L}'$ to the corresponding elements of $\mathbf{M}'_{(1)}$.

For $\mathbf{P}_{(2)}$, the next approximation to $\mathbf{P}$, we first calculate

$$\mathbf{P}^*_{(2)} = (\mathbf{J}_{(1)}{}^{-1}\mathbf{L}'_{(1)}\mathbf{V}_{(1)}{}^{-1}\mathbf{A}\mathbf{V}_{(1)}{}^{-1}\mathbf{L}_{(1)}-\mathbf{I})\mathbf{J}_{(1)}{}^{-1}$$

and then, if necessary, standardize it so that all diagonal elements are unity; this gives $\mathbf{P}_{(2)}$. The next approximation to $\mathbf{V}$ is given by

$$\mathbf{V}_{(2)} = \mathrm{diag}(\mathbf{A}-\mathbf{L}_{(2)}\mathbf{P}_{(2)}\mathbf{L}'_{(2)}).$$

As far as the first iteration is concerned this method is identical with that proposed by Howe. For later iterations he suggests a slightly different procedure with the object of increasing the rate of convergence, but we have not investigated it fully.

6.7. Numerical example

To illustrate the iterative method of solution we use the same data as before. The pattern of factor loadings previously assumed would not now lead to a unique set of loadings, since with corrrelated factors any non-singular linear transformation may be applied. Thus the first row of loadings could be replaced by a linear combination of all three rows, the second and third rows being left unaltered. To ensure uniqueness we make the hypothesis that the pattern of loadings is as follows:

$$\begin{matrix} x & x & 0 & 0 & x & x & x & x \\ x & x & x & 0 & 0 & 0 & 0 & 0 \\ 0 & x & x & x & x & x & x & 0 \end{matrix}$$

To obtain an initial approximation to $\mathbf{L}'$, we pre-multiplied the matrix of final loadings for the orthogonal case by a matrix $\mathbf{T}$ given by

$$\mathbf{T} = \begin{bmatrix} 1{\cdot}0000 & -0{\cdot}3097 & -0{\cdot}6416 \\ 0 & 1{\cdot}0469 & 0 \\ 0 & 0 & 1{\cdot}1881 \end{bmatrix}.$$

This was chosen so that the third and fourth loadings of the first row are zero, and the diagonal elements of $(\mathbf{TT}')^{-1}$ are all unity. The initial approximation to $\mathbf{P}$ is given by

$$(\mathbf{TT}')^{-1} = \begin{bmatrix} 1{\cdot}000 & 0{\cdot}296 & 0{\cdot}540 \\ 0{\cdot}296 & 1{\cdot}000 & 0{\cdot}160 \\ 0{\cdot}540 & 0{\cdot}160 & 1{\cdot}000 \end{bmatrix}$$

and this enables an approximation for $\mathbf{V}$ to be found.

Starting from these values, three iterations were performed. The calculations for the last of these are reproduced below, with $\mathbf{L}'_{(1)}$, $\mathbf{V}_{(1)}$ and $\mathbf{P}_{(1)}$ representing the values obtained from the preceding iteration:

$\mathbf{L}_{(1)}$	0·307	0·245	0	0	0·599	0·648	0·440	0·606
	0·653	0·691	0·774	0	0	0	0	0
	0	0·211	0·389	0·663	0·385	0·216	0·414	0
$\mathbf{V}_{(1)}$	0·3603	0·2171	0·1581	0·5604	0·2430	0·3817	0·4375	0·6328
$\mathbf{L}'_{(1)}\mathbf{V}_{(1)}^{-1}$	0·852	1·129	0	0	2·465	1·698	1·006	0·958
	1·812	3·183	4·896	0	0	0	0	0
	0	0·972	2·460	1·183	1·584	0·566	0·946	0

$$\mathbf{J}_{(1)} = \begin{bmatrix} 4{\cdot}1375 & 1{\cdot}3362 & 1{\cdot}9702 \\ 1{\cdot}3362 & 7{\cdot}1721 & 2{\cdot}5760 \\ 1{\cdot}9702 & 2{\cdot}5760 & 3{\cdot}0706 \end{bmatrix}$$

$$\mathbf{J}_{(1)}^{-1} = \begin{bmatrix} 0{\cdot}35047 & 0{\cdot}02215 & -0{\cdot}24345 \\ 0{\cdot}02215 & 0{\cdot}20096 & -0{\cdot}18280 \\ -0{\cdot}24345 & -0{\cdot}18280 & 0{\cdot}63523 \end{bmatrix}$$

$$\mathbf{P}_{(1)} = \begin{bmatrix} 1\cdot000 & 0\cdot297 & 0\cdot542 \\ 0\cdot297 & 1\cdot000 & 0\cdot152 \\ 0\cdot542 & 0\cdot152 & 1\cdot000 \end{bmatrix}$$

$$(\mathbf{P}_{(1)}^{-1}+\mathbf{J}_{(1)})^{-1} = \begin{bmatrix} 0\cdot18796 & -0\cdot00863 & -0\cdot04523 \\ -0\cdot00863 & 0\cdot14802 & -0\cdot08314 \\ -0\cdot04523 & -0\cdot08314 & 0\cdot28295 \end{bmatrix}$$

									Row sums
$\mathbf{L}'_{(1)}\mathbf{V}_{(1)}^{-1}\mathbf{A}$	3·896	4·529	3·939	2·906	5·664	5·212	4·764	3·996	34·906
	7·336	8·308	8·644	2·714	4·659	3·924	4·212	2·863	42·660
	3·710	4·751	4·962	3·605	4·781	3·989	4·303	2·656	32·757

									Row sums
$\mathbf{M}'_{(1)}$	0·5012	0·5647	(0·4413)	(0·3597)	0·8082	0·7654	0·6645	0·6062	4·7112
	0·7438	0·7957	0·8330	(0·0769)	(0·2433)	(0·2042)	(0·2246)	(0·1685)	3·2900
	(0·2636)	0·4487	0·5072	0·6630	0·7093	0·5667	0·6519	(0·3327)	4·1431

$\mathbf{L}'_{(2)}$	0·3074	0·2454	0	0	0·6000	0·6489	0·4406	0·6062
	0·6525	0·6908	0·7738	0	0	0	0	0
	0	0·2107	0·3896	0·6630	0·3841	0·2150	0·4131	0

$$\mathbf{P}^*_{(2)} = \begin{bmatrix} 1\cdot0009 & 0\cdot2978 & 0\cdot5423 \\ 0\cdot2978 & 0\cdot9999 & 0\cdot1514 \\ 0\cdot5423 & 0\cdot1514 & 0\cdot9993 \end{bmatrix} \qquad \mathbf{P}_{(2)} = \begin{bmatrix} 1\cdot0000 & 0\cdot2977 & 0\cdot5423 \\ 0\cdot2977 & 1\cdot0000 & 0\cdot1515 \\ 0\cdot5423 & 0\cdot1515 & 1\cdot0000 \end{bmatrix}$$

$\mathbf{V}_{(2)}$	0·3603	0·2171	0·1581	0·5604	0·2425	0·3814	0·4378	0·6325

As an example of the way in which the non-zero elements of $\mathbf{L}'_{(2)}$ are obtained from the elements of $\mathbf{M}'_{(1)}$, consider the values in the first column and denote them by x_1 and x_2. Then these values are given by the equations

$$\begin{bmatrix} 1\cdot000 & 0\cdot297 \\ 0\cdot297 & 1\cdot000 \end{bmatrix} \begin{bmatrix} x_1 \\ x_2 \end{bmatrix} = \begin{bmatrix} 0\cdot5012 \\ 0\cdot7438 \end{bmatrix}.$$

Hence $x_1 = 0\cdot3074$ and $x_2 = 0\cdot6525$. Similarly, for the values in the fifth column we have

$$\begin{bmatrix} 1\cdot000 & 0\cdot542 \\ 0\cdot542 & 1\cdot000 \end{bmatrix} \begin{bmatrix} x_1 \\ x_3 \end{bmatrix} = \begin{bmatrix} 0\cdot8082 \\ 0\cdot7093 \end{bmatrix},$$

and so $x_1 = 0\cdot6000$ and $x_3 = 0\cdot3841$. In each case the matrix on the left-hand side is either $\mathbf{P}_{(1)}$ or a symmetric sub-matrix of $\mathbf{P}_{(1)}$. The bracketed values in $\mathbf{M}'_{(1)}$ are not required here.

It is difficult to say how near the above values are to the exact solutions of the equations of estimation, but they are sufficiently good for our purposes. It is evident that further iterations would not appreciably improve the fit.

6.8. Tests of significance

We now discuss the provision of satisfactory tests of the hypotheses made in the foregoing sections that the p variates x_i depend on precisely k common factors, either correlated or uncorrelated, and that certain specified loadings are zero. The argument at the beginning of Section (2.6) still holds good, and the large-sample χ^2 criterion based on the likelihood ratio is as given by expression (2.12). The process of evaluating this expression requires modification, however, and the number of degrees of freedom for χ^2 is not the same as before. We should expect the χ^2 approximation to be improved, as in Chapter 2, by the replacement of n in (2.12) by a suitable multiplying factor, though what this should be is to some extent a matter for conjecture. It seems best to use the value which is correct for $k = 0$. The criterion will therefore be taken as

$$n'\{\log_e(|\hat{\mathbf{C}}|/|\mathbf{A}|) + \mathrm{tr}(\mathbf{A}\hat{\mathbf{C}}^{-1}) - p\}, \tag{6.12}$$

where

$$n' = n - \tfrac{1}{6}(2p+5).$$

For maximum likelihood estimates we found, both for correlated and for uncorrelated factors, that

$$\mathrm{diag}(\mathbf{I} - \hat{\mathbf{C}}^{-1}\mathbf{A}) = 0$$

Hence $\mathrm{tr}(\mathbf{A}\hat{\mathbf{C}}^{-1}) = p$, and expression (6.12) may be simplified, as before, to

$$n' \log_e(|\hat{\mathbf{C}}|/|\mathbf{A}|). \tag{6.13}$$

At this point it is convenient to discuss separately the procedures for the two cases.

Let us first suppose that the factors are uncorrelated. If exact, or nearly exact, maximum likelihood estimates have been obtained, the value of χ^2 may be found from (6.13). The value of $|\hat{\mathbf{C}}|$ is calculated by using (2.16). If, on the other hand, the equations of estimation have not been solved exactly, it is necessary to use expression (6.12). To simplify the calculation of $\text{tr}(\mathbf{A}\hat{\mathbf{C}}^{-1})$ we note that

$$\hat{\mathbf{C}}^{-1} = \hat{\mathbf{V}}^{-1} - \hat{\mathbf{C}}^{-1}\hat{\mathbf{L}}\hat{\mathbf{L}}'\hat{\mathbf{V}}^{-1}.$$

It follows that

$$\mathbf{A}\hat{\mathbf{C}}^{-1} = (\mathbf{A} - \mathbf{M}\hat{\mathbf{L}}')\hat{\mathbf{V}}^{-1},$$

where $\mathbf{M}' = \hat{\mathbf{L}}'\hat{\mathbf{C}}^{-1}\mathbf{A}$, and hence that

$$\text{tr}(\mathbf{A}\hat{\mathbf{C}}^{-1}) = \text{tr}(\mathbf{A}\hat{\mathbf{V}}^{-1}) - \text{tr}(\hat{\mathbf{L}}'\hat{\mathbf{V}}^{-1}\mathbf{M}).$$

The matrix $\mathbf{M}$ is, of course, calculated in each iteration.

When n is reasonably large a simple approximation for the value of χ^2 may be used. We have

$$\begin{aligned} n' \log_e (|\hat{\mathbf{C}}|/|\mathbf{A}|) &= -n' \log_e |\hat{\mathbf{C}}^{-1}\mathbf{A}| \\ &= -n' \log_e |\hat{\mathbf{V}}^{-1}(\mathbf{A} - \hat{\mathbf{L}}\mathbf{M}')| \\ &= -n' \log_e |\mathbf{I} + \mathbf{X}|, \end{aligned}$$

where $$\mathbf{X} = [x_{ij}] = \hat{\mathbf{V}}^{-1}(\mathbf{A} - \hat{\mathbf{V}} - \hat{\mathbf{L}}\mathbf{M}').$$

The diagonal elements of $\mathbf{X}$ are zero and the non-diagonal elements tend to be small when n is large. Hence, if we expand $|\mathbf{I}+\mathbf{X}|$ retaining only second degree terms in the x_{ij}, we obtain as an approximation to the criterion of (6.13) the expression

$$n' \sum_{i<j} x_{ij}x_{ji}. \tag{6.14}$$

The matrix $\mathbf{A} - \hat{\mathbf{V}} - \hat{\mathbf{L}}\mathbf{M}'$ is similar to the usual residual matrix, but is not symmetric. The above method of calculation is simpler than direct use of the residuals.

If m is the number of non-zero loadings, which are assumed to be uniquely determined, the number of degrees of freedom for χ^2 is

$$\begin{aligned} &\tfrac{1}{2}p(p+1) - p - m \\ &= \tfrac{1}{2}p(p-1) - m. \end{aligned}$$

In the case of correlated factors the same results still apply, apart from a few simple alterations. Since $\hat{\mathbf{C}}$ is given by

$\hat{\mathbf{L}}\hat{\mathbf{P}}\hat{\mathbf{L}}'+\hat{\mathbf{V}}$ we now have

$$\begin{aligned}|\hat{\mathbf{C}}| &= |\hat{\mathbf{V}}(\mathbf{I}_p+\hat{\mathbf{V}}^{-1}\hat{\mathbf{L}}\hat{\mathbf{P}}\hat{\mathbf{L}}')| \\ &= |\hat{\mathbf{V}}|\times|\mathbf{I}_p+\hat{\mathbf{V}}^{-1}\hat{\mathbf{L}}\hat{\mathbf{P}}\hat{\mathbf{L}}'| \\ &= |\hat{\mathbf{V}}|\times|\mathbf{I}_k+(\hat{\mathbf{P}}\hat{\mathbf{L}}'\hat{\mathbf{V}}^{-1}\hat{\mathbf{L}})|\end{aligned}$$

The expression for $\mathrm{tr}(\mathbf{A}\hat{\mathbf{C}}^{-1})$ is the same as before if we now define $\mathbf{M}'$ to be $\hat{\mathbf{P}}\hat{\mathbf{L}}'\hat{\mathbf{C}}^{-1}\mathbf{A}$, which is how it appears in the iterations. The approximate criterion (6.14) is also calculated as before. Since we have to estimate the factor correlation coefficients ρ_{rs}, the number of degrees of freedom is reduced by $\frac{1}{2}k(k-1)$ and becomes

$$\tfrac{1}{2}(p-k)(p+k-1)-m.$$

Values of χ^2 were calculated for the data previously analysed, though tests of significance are not really justifiable here. We have $n = 210$, $p = 8$, $k = 3$ and $n' = 206{\cdot}5$. For uncorrelated factors the number m of non-zero loadings is 17, so that the number of degrees of freedom is 11. Using the estimates of the loadings obtained on the desk machine and the approximate method the value of χ^2 was found to be 5·0. When the loadings given by the computer were used and expression (6.13) was employed the value of χ^2 was reduced to 4·1. In either case the value is well below expectation and leads us to accept the hypothesis. This conclusion is not surprising since, as already remarked, the hypothesis was set up only after a previous analysis of the same data. For correlated factors the value of χ^2 was again approximately 5·0, but now $m = 15$ and the number of degrees of freedom is 10.

6.9. Summary and conclusions

In this chapter we have shown that, for various hypotheses, it is possible to solve numerically the maximum likelihood equations of estimation and to test the hypotheses. But it is evident that, when desk computers are used, the labour involved will increase very quickly as the number of factors increases. If $k > 3$ an electronic digital computer becomes almost a necessity if an exact solution is required, since the convergence of the iterative procedures is usually very slow. On the other hand it seems likely that in practice a few iterations would often be sufficient to obtain a reasonably good fit and to enable a satisfactory test of significance to be made.

REFERENCES

Anderson, T. W. and Rubin, H. (1955), Statistical inference in factor analysis, *Proc. Third Berkeley Symposium* **5,** 111–150

Emmett, W. G. (1949), Evidence of a space factor at 11+ and after, *Brit. J. Psychol. Statist. Sect.* **2,** 3–16

Howe, W. G. (1955), Some contributions to factor analysis, *U.S.A.E.C. Rep.* ORNL–1919

Lawley, D. N. (1958), Estimation in factor analysis under various initial assumptions, *Brit. J. Statist. Psychol.* **11,** 1–12

Nixon, W. L. B., Gallagher, G. and Maxwell, A E. (1962), Mercury programme for estimating factor loadings under various initial assumptions, *Laboratory Notes,* University of London Computer Unit

7
THE ESTIMATION OF FACTOR SCORES

7.1. Introduction

In previous chapters we have been concerned almost exclusively with deciding the number and nature of the common factors and with estimating their loadings in the variates. While these problems constitute the main interest of factor analysis, it is sometimes desirable in practice to go a step further and find equations by which the scores on the hypothetical factors may be estimated from a set of observations of the variates. This problem will now be considered.

7.2. The regression method with uncorrelated factors

To begin with let us suppose that the factors are uncorrelated and that, by some method, loadings and residual variances have been estimated, forming matrices $\mathbf{L} = [l_{ir}]$ and $\mathbf{V} = [v_i]$ (circumflex accents are here omitted). As before, the estimated covariance matrix for the x_i is $\mathbf{C} = \mathbf{LL}'+\mathbf{V}$.

For a given set of observations of the p variates x_i we clearly cannot estimate, in the usual statistical sense, the values of the k factors f_r and of the p residuals e_i since the number of hypothetical variates exceeds the number of observed variates. We can, however, find linear functions of the x_i which in some sense provide reasonable estimates of the f_r.

If the true values of the f_r were known we could choose their estimates $\hat{f}_r$ in such a way as to minimize, for each value of r, the sum of squares $\Sigma(f_r-\hat{f}_r)^2$, where Σ denotes summation over the sample. Since $\hat{f}_r$ is a linear function of the x_i this 'least squares' method would be the same as finding the linear regression of f_r on the x_i. The coefficients of linear regression would be given in terms of the covariances between f_r and the x_i and of the variances and covariances of the x_i. The former cannot be calculated in the usual way, but it seems reasonable to use as estimates for them the elements of the vector

$$\mathbf{l}'_r = [l_{1r}\, l_{2r} \,...\, l_{pr}],$$

which is the rth row of $\mathbf{L}'$. For the variances and covariances of the x_i we use the matrix $\mathbf{C}$.

The estimates for the f_r are then given by

$$\hat{f}_r = \mathbf{l}'_r\mathbf{C}^{-1}\mathbf{x} \quad (r = 1, 2, ..., k),$$

where $\mathbf{x}$ is the column vector $\{x_1, x_2 ... x_p\}$. These equations may be written in the form

$$\hat{\mathbf{f}} = \mathbf{L}'\mathbf{C}^{-1}\mathbf{x}, \tag{7.1}$$

or

$$\hat{\mathbf{f}} = (\mathbf{I}+\mathbf{J})^{-1}\mathbf{L}'\mathbf{V}^{-1}\mathbf{x}, \tag{7.2}$$

where

$$\hat{\mathbf{f}} = \{\hat{f}_1\, \hat{f}_2\, ...\, \hat{f}_k\},$$

and, as before, $\mathbf{J} = \mathbf{L}'\mathbf{V}^{-1}\mathbf{L}$.

Whereas the covariance matrix for the f_r is the unit matrix of order k, that for the estimates $\hat{f}_r$ is, if we neglect sampling errors in $\mathbf{L}$ and $\mathbf{V}$,

$$\begin{aligned}&(\mathbf{L}'\mathbf{C}^{-1})\mathbf{C}(\mathbf{C}^{-1}\mathbf{L})\\ &= \mathbf{L}'\mathbf{C}^{-1}\mathbf{L}\\ &= \mathbf{I}-(\mathbf{I}+\mathbf{J})^{-1}.\end{aligned} \tag{7.3}$$

The covariance matrix for the errors of estimation $\hat{f}_r - f_r$ is

$$\begin{aligned}&\mathbf{I}-\mathbf{L}'\mathbf{C}^{-1}\mathbf{L}\\ &= (\mathbf{I}+\mathbf{J})^{-1}.\end{aligned} \tag{7.4}$$

This method was first given by Thomson (see Thomson, 1951, and references given there) and was termed by him the regression method. With slight modification it can also be used with correlated factors.

7.3. The regression method with correlated factors

If the factors are correlated and their estimated correlation matrix is denoted by $\mathbf{P}$, as in Chapter 6, then the only changes required are that the covariances between the f_r and the x_i should be estimated by the matrix $\mathbf{PL}'$ and that we now put $\mathbf{C} = \mathbf{LPL}'+\mathbf{V}$. We thus have

$$\hat{\mathbf{f}} = \mathbf{PL}'\mathbf{C}^{-1}\mathbf{x}, \tag{7.5}$$

or

$$\hat{\mathbf{f}} = (\mathbf{P}^{-1}+\mathbf{J})^{-1}\mathbf{L}'\mathbf{V}^{-1}\mathbf{x}. \tag{7.6}$$

The covariance matrix for the estimates $\hat{f}_r$ is now

$$\begin{aligned} &\mathbf{PL'C^{-1}LP} \\ &= (\mathbf{P}^{-1}+\mathbf{J})^{-1}\mathbf{JP} \\ &= \mathbf{P}-(\mathbf{P}^{-1}+\mathbf{J})^{-1}, \end{aligned} \tag{7.7}$$

while that for the errors $\hat{f}_r - f_r$ is

$$(\mathbf{P}^{-1}+\mathbf{J})^{-1}. \tag{7.8}$$

7.4. Minimizing the residuals

An alternative method of procedure for estimating factor scores is due to Bartlett (1938). Here the principle adopted is the minimization, for a given set of observations, of

$$\sum_i e_i^2/v_i,$$

which is the sum of squares of standardized residuals. The summation in this case is over variates. The above sum of squares may be written as

$$\sum_{i=1}^{p} (x_i - \sum_r l_{ir} f_r)^2/v_i,$$

which must be minimized with respect to $f_1, f_2, ..., f_k$. This leads to the equations

$$\sum_{i,s} (l_{ir} l_{is}/v_i)\check{f}_s = \sum_i (l_{ir} x_i/v_i) \quad (r = 1, 2, ..., k),$$

where the estimate of f_r is now denoted by $\check{f}_r$. These equations may be written as

$$(\mathbf{L'V^{-1}L})\check{\mathbf{f}} = \mathbf{L'V^{-1}x},$$

or

$$\check{\mathbf{f}} = \mathbf{J^{-1}L'V^{-1}x}. \tag{7.9}$$

Though the sets of estimates obtained by the two methods have been reached by entirely different approaches, a comparison of (7.2) and (7.9) shows that, for uncorrelated factors, they are simply related by the equation,

$$\check{\mathbf{f}} = (\mathbf{I}+\mathbf{J}^{-1})\hat{\mathbf{f}}. \tag{7.10}$$

Similarly, for correlated factors, we have

$$\check{\mathbf{f}} = (\mathbf{I}+\mathbf{J}^{-1}\mathbf{P}^{-1})\hat{\mathbf{f}}. \tag{7.11}$$

7.5. A numerical example

As an example of the estimation of factor scores (with uncorrelated factors) we shall take $\mathbf{L}'$ to be the matrix of loadings given in Table 3.7, and we shall use the regression method. The elements of $\mathbf{V}$ are obtained by subtracting the values in the third row of that table from unity, and are thus:

$$(0{\cdot}519 \quad 0{\cdot}588 \quad 0{\cdot}643 \quad 0{\cdot}400 \quad 0{\cdot}417 \quad 0{\cdot}621).$$

Using these data we find

$$\mathbf{L}'\mathbf{V}^{-1} = \begin{bmatrix} 1{\cdot}168 & 1{\cdot}039 & 0{\cdot}712 & 1{\cdot}708 & 1{\cdot}645 & 0{\cdot}926 \\ 0{\cdot}649 & 0{\cdot}335 & 0{\cdot}597 & -0{\cdot}912 & -0{\cdot}803 & -0{\cdot}356 \end{bmatrix}$$

$$\mathbf{J} = \begin{bmatrix} 4{\cdot}496 & -0{\cdot}507 \\ -0{\cdot}507 & 1{\cdot}195 \end{bmatrix}, \quad (\mathbf{I}+\mathbf{J})^{-1} = \begin{bmatrix} 0{\cdot}1860 & 0{\cdot}0430 \\ 0{\cdot}0430 & 0{\cdot}4655 \end{bmatrix}.$$

Hence the matrix of coefficients, $(\mathbf{I}+\mathbf{J})^{-1}\mathbf{L}'\mathbf{V}^{-1}$, is

$$\begin{bmatrix} 0{\cdot}245 & 0{\cdot}208 & 0{\cdot}158 & 0{\cdot}278 & 0{\cdot}271 & 0{\cdot}157 \\ 0{\cdot}352 & 0{\cdot}201 & 0{\cdot}309 & -0{\cdot}351 & -0{\cdot}303 & -0{\cdot}126 \end{bmatrix}$$

and the covariance matrix for the estimated factor scores is found from (7.3) to be

$$\begin{bmatrix} 0{\cdot}8140 & -0{\cdot}0430 \\ -0{\cdot}0430 & 0{\cdot}5345 \end{bmatrix}.$$

The equation for estimating scores on the first factor is, for example,

$$\hat{f}_1 = 0{\cdot}245x_1 + 0{\cdot}208x_2 + \ldots + 0{\cdot}157x_6,$$

where the x's are standardized variate scores. A similar equation may be written out for the second factor.

REFERENCES

Thomson, G. H. (1951), *The Factorial Analysis of Human Ability*, 5th ed., London University Press

Bartlett, M. S. (1938), Methods of estimating mental factors, *Nature* **141**, 609–610

8
IDENTIFYING FACTORS IN DIFFERENT POPULATIONS

8.1. Introduction

In this last chapter we shall consider the problem of comparing and combining results obtained from different sources. We shall suppose that random samples have been drawn from each of two multivariate normal populations with different covariance matrices. The question which then naturally arises is whether the same factors are operating in each case. This problem and others related to it have been discussed by earlier writers, notably Thomson and Thurstone in their respective textbooks (Thomson, 1951; Thurstone, 1947), and elsewhere.

Thomson was particularly interested in the effect produced on factors by selection of one or more of the variates. By employing Karl Pearson's selection formulae (Pearson, 1912; Aitken, 1934) he was able to show that such selection may cause factors which were originally orthogonal to become correlated. A further complication is that additional factors may be introduced having loadings in the variates directly selected. It follows that for purposes of comparison it is as a rule useless to perform separate factorial analyses on covariance or correlation matrices obtained by sampling two different populations, especially if the factors are restricted to being orthogonal in each case. For when more than one common factor is involved it becomes difficult to discover the relation between the factors derived from one analysis and those derived from another.

As a result of these findings Thomson came to somewhat pessimistic conclusions regarding the permanence of factors, even for a given set of variates. A more hopeful attitude was adopted by Thurstone, who went some way towards overcoming the difficulties by employing 'oblique', or correlated, factors and by imposing his idea of 'simple structure'. To make further progress, however, a fresh approach seemed to be necessary, and this has led us to propose a new model. In this model the basic assumption is that any selective process operates directly on the factors and only indirectly on the variates. Any two populations are assumed to differ only as regards the variances and covariances of the factor scores. The value of the model depends ultimately, of course, upon how well it works in practice.

8.2. A hypothesis for two populations

Let us suppose that for each of two p-variate normal populations the same k common factors are in operation. The covariance matrices for the factors in the two populations will be denoted by $\mathbf{\Gamma}_1$ and $\mathbf{\Gamma}_2$. The relationship between the variates x_i and the factors f_r is, as before, given by eqs (1.1). The coefficients l_{ir} in these equations are invariant under changes of population and therefore the loading matrix $\mathbf{L}$ is the same for both populations. We shall make what seems a reasonable assumption, that the residual variances are the same for both populations and that they form a matrix $\mathbf{V}$. (The model can be generalized to some extent by allowing the populations to have different residual variance matrices, $\mathbf{V}_1$ and $\mathbf{V}_2$, but this complicates the subsequent estimation procedures and we shall not discuss it here.) The population covariance matrices for the x_i are thus given respectively by

$$\begin{aligned} \mathbf{C}_1 &= \mathbf{L}\mathbf{\Gamma}_1\mathbf{L}' + \mathbf{V}, \\ \mathbf{C}_2 &= \mathbf{L}\mathbf{\Gamma}_2\mathbf{L}' + \mathbf{V}. \end{aligned} \tag{8.1}$$

For convenience we shall make the assumption, which is likely to be satisfied in practice, that $\mathbf{\Gamma}_1$ and $\mathbf{\Gamma}_2$ are both non-singular. As in Chapter 6 we shall suppose that certain of the loadings are zero. The number and positions of these must be such as to determine the factors uniquely apart from their directions and scales. The scales of the factors are of course arbitrary. It will be convenient to choose them in such a way that

$$\text{diag}(\mathbf{\Gamma}) = \mathbf{I}, \tag{8.2}$$

where

$$\mathbf{\Gamma} = (n_1\mathbf{\Gamma}_1 + n_2\mathbf{\Gamma}_2)/(n_1+n_2)$$

and where n_1 and n_2 are as in the following section.

Thus the hypothesis set up is that there are precisely k factors, that certain specified elements of the loading matrix $\mathbf{L}$ are zero and that the population covariance matrices satisfy the relations (8.1).

8.3 The estimation procedure

Let $\mathbf{A}_1$ and $\mathbf{A}_2$ be the usual sample covariance matrices with respectively n_1 and n_2 degrees of freedom, obtained by taking a random sample from each population. We might in practice begin by examining whether the hypothesis that $\mathbf{C}_1 = \mathbf{C}_2$ is tenable. This could if necessary be tested by means of the criterion

$$n \log_e |\mathbf{A}| - n_1 \log_e |\mathbf{A}_1| - n_2 \log_e |\mathbf{A}_2|, \tag{8.3}$$

where $n = n_1 + n_2$ and where

$$\mathbf{A} = (n_1\mathbf{A}_1 + n_2\mathbf{A}_2)/(n_1 + n_2).$$

Under the hypothesis the criterion is distributed approximately as χ^2 with $\frac{1}{2}p(p+1)$ degrees of freedom. The approximation is improved (Box, 1949) if the expression (8.3) is multiplied by the factor

$$1 - \frac{1}{6}\left(2p + 1 - \frac{2}{p+1}\right)\left(\frac{1}{n_1} + \frac{1}{n_2} - \frac{1}{n}\right).$$

A more specific test will be mentioned later.

If the hypothesis $\mathbf{C}_1 = \mathbf{C}_2$ were accepted, a factor analysis would be performed on the pooled covariance matrix $\mathbf{A}$; but we shall in fact suppose that it is rejected and that the hypothesis of the previous section is instead set up. Then the log-likelihood function is, omitting a function of the observations,

$$-\tfrac{1}{2}n_1\{\log_e |\mathbf{C}_1| + \operatorname{tr}(\mathbf{A}_1\mathbf{C}_1^{-1})\} - \tfrac{1}{2}n_2\{\log_e |\mathbf{C}_2| + \operatorname{tr}(\mathbf{A}_2\mathbf{C}_2^{-1})\}. \tag{8.4}$$

To estimate the unknown parameters we maximize this with respect to the non-zero elements of $\mathbf{L}$, the elements of $\mathbf{V}$, and the elements of $\mathbf{\Gamma}_1$ and $\mathbf{\Gamma}_2$, subject to (8.2). The resulting equations of estimation are:

$$n_1\mathbf{\Gamma}_1(\mathbf{L}'\mathbf{C}_1^{-1} - \mathbf{L}'\mathbf{C}_1^{-1}\mathbf{A}_1\mathbf{C}_1^{-1}) + n_2\mathbf{\Gamma}_2(\mathbf{L}'\mathbf{C}_2^{-1} - \mathbf{L}'\mathbf{C}_2^{-1}\mathbf{A}_2\mathbf{C}_2^{-1}) \overset{*}{=} 0, \tag{8.5}$$

$$n_1 \operatorname{diag}(\mathbf{C}_1^{-1} - \mathbf{C}_1^{-1}\mathbf{A}_1\mathbf{C}_1^{-1}) + n_2 \operatorname{diag}(\mathbf{C}_2^{-1} - \mathbf{C}_2^{-1}\mathbf{A}_2\mathbf{C}_2^{-1}) = 0, \tag{8.6}$$

$$\mathbf{L}'\mathbf{C}_\alpha^{-1}(\mathbf{C}_\alpha - \mathbf{A}_\alpha)\mathbf{C}_\alpha^{-1}\mathbf{L} = 0 \quad (\alpha = 1, 2), \tag{8.7}$$

where the sign $\overset{*}{=}$ means that elements of the two sides are to be equated only when they correspond in position to non-zero elements of $\mathbf{L}'$.

The above equations may be simplified in the same way as those of Chapter 6 and may be solved by an iterative procedure. Let capital letters without circumflex accents refer to estimates used to begin a cycle of iteration. The improved estimates obtained as a result of this cycle will be denoted by letters with circumflex accents.

We begin by finding

$$\mathbf{J} = \mathbf{L}'\mathbf{V}^{-1}\mathbf{L},$$

$$\mathbf{M}'_\alpha = \mathbf{\Gamma}_\alpha\mathbf{L}'\mathbf{C}_\alpha^{-1}\mathbf{A}_\alpha = (\mathbf{\Gamma}_\alpha^{-1}+\mathbf{J})^{-1}\mathbf{L}'\mathbf{V}^{-1}\mathbf{A}_\alpha \quad (\alpha = 1, 2) \tag{8.8}$$

and

$$\mathbf{M}' = (n_1\mathbf{M}'_1+n_2\mathbf{M}'_2)/(n_1+n_2).$$

Then, with $\mathbf{\Gamma}$ as before, improved estimates of the loadings are given by

$$\mathbf{\Gamma}\mathbf{L}' \overset{*}{=} \mathbf{M}'. \tag{8.9}$$

We next calculate

$$\mathbf{Z}_\alpha = \mathbf{L}'\mathbf{V}^{-1}\mathbf{A}_\alpha\mathbf{V}^{-1}\mathbf{L}, \tag{8.10}$$

$$\mathbf{\Gamma}_\alpha^* = (\mathbf{J}^{-1}\mathbf{Z}_\alpha-\mathbf{I})\mathbf{J}^{-1} \quad (\alpha = 1, 2) \tag{8.11}$$

and

$$\mathbf{\Gamma}^* = (n_1\mathbf{\Gamma}_1^*+n_2\mathbf{\Gamma}_2^*)/(n_1+n_2).$$

Let $\mathbf{D}$ be the diagonal matrix such that

$$\operatorname{diag}(\mathbf{D}\mathbf{\Gamma}^*\mathbf{D}) = \mathbf{I}.$$

Then better estimates of the factor covariance matrices are given by

$$\hat{\mathbf{\Gamma}}_\alpha = \mathbf{D}\mathbf{\Gamma}_\alpha^*\mathbf{D} \quad (\alpha = 1, 2). \tag{8.12}$$

We find also

$$\hat{\mathbf{\Gamma}} = \mathbf{D}\mathbf{\Gamma}^*\mathbf{D} = (n_1\hat{\mathbf{\Gamma}}_1+n_2\hat{\mathbf{\Gamma}}_2)/(n_1+n_2).$$

Improved estimates of the residual variances are given by

$$\hat{\mathbf{V}} = \operatorname{diag}(\mathbf{A}-\hat{\mathbf{L}}\hat{\mathbf{\Gamma}}\hat{\mathbf{L}}') \tag{8.13}$$

8.4. Testing hypotheses

The hypothesis which has been set up may be tested by the criterion

$$n_1 \log_e(|\hat{\mathbf{C}}_1|/|\mathbf{A}_1|)+n_2 \log_e(|\hat{\mathbf{C}}_2|/|\mathbf{A}_2|) \tag{8.14}$$

where circumflex accents now refer to final maximum likelihood estimates. Under the hypothesis this criterion is distributed for large samples approximately as χ^2 with p^2-k^2-m degrees of freedom, where m is the number of non-zero loadings. In the trivial case where $k = 0$ the approximation is improved if expression (8.14) is multiplied by

$$1-\frac{1}{12}\left(2p+3-\frac{1}{p}\right)\left(\frac{1}{n_1}+\frac{1}{n_2}\right)+\frac{1}{3pn}.$$

When $k > 0$ the correct value for the multiplying factor is unknown, but with sufficient accuracy it may probably be taken simply as

$$1-\frac{1}{12}(2p+3)\left(\frac{1}{n_1}+\frac{1}{n_2}\right).$$

For reasonably large samples an approximation to expression (8.14) may be obtained by finding the matrices

$$\mathbf{X}_\alpha = [x_{ij(\alpha)}] = \hat{\mathbf{V}}^{-1}(\mathbf{A}_\alpha-\hat{\mathbf{L}}\mathbf{M}'_\alpha-\hat{\mathbf{V}}) \quad (\alpha = 1, 2).$$

We then have

$$\log_e(|\hat{\mathbf{C}}_\alpha|/|\mathbf{A}_\alpha|) \approx \tfrac{1}{2}\sum_i x_{ii}{}^2{}_{(\alpha)}+\sum_{i<j} x_{ij(\alpha)}x_{ji(\alpha)}. \qquad (8.15)$$

The approximation is valid even when the maximum likelihood equations have not been solved exactly.

The hypothesis that $\mathbf{\Gamma}_1 = \mathbf{\Gamma}_2$ may if necessary be tested by use of the criterion

$$n \log_e|\mathbf{Z}|-n_1 \log_e|\mathbf{Z}_1|-n_2 \log_e|\mathbf{Z}_2|, \qquad (8.16)$$

where $\mathbf{Z}_1$ and $\mathbf{Z}_2$ are as in (8.10) and where

$$\mathbf{Z} = (n_1\mathbf{Z}_1+n_2\mathbf{Z}_2)/(n_1+n_2).$$

Under the hypothesis this is distributed approximately as χ^2 with $\frac{1}{2}k(k+1)$ degrees of freedom. This test has much greater sensitivity than the more general one provided by the criterion (8.3).

The criterion (8.16) is not exactly that derived by the likelihood ratio method, but is very similar and is more easily computed. We might expect that it would be improved by the multiplying factor

$$1-\frac{1}{6}\left(2k+1-\frac{2}{k+1}\right)\left(\frac{1}{n_1}+\frac{1}{n_2}-\frac{1}{n}\right),$$

though strictly this could be justified only if the estimates of the loadings and residual variances in (8.10) were replaced by their true values.

8.5. Numerical example

To illustrate the calculations, data for a sample of 205 boys and a sample of 87 girls of average age 11 years on six cognitive variates are used. The variates are six sub-tests from the Wechsler Intelligence Scale for Children, namely (1) Comprehension, (2) Similarities, (3) Vocabulary, (4) Picture Arrangement, (5) Block Design, and (6) Coding. The covariance matrices for these variates for the boys ($\mathbf{A}_1$), the girls ($\mathbf{A}_2$) and for both sexes ($\mathbf{A}$) are given in Table 8.1, the respective degrees of freedom being $n_1 = 204$, $n_2 = 86$ and $n = 290$.

Table 8.1. Covariance matrices for six variates for boys, girls and for both sexes

Variates	*1*	*2*	*3*	*4*	*5*	*6*	*Row sums*
			Boys: $\mathbf{A}_1(n_1 = 204)$				
1	0·954	0·650	0·646	0·629	0·440	0·580	3·899
2	0·650	0·917	0·651	0·561	0·504	0·537	3·820
3	0·646	0·651	0·943	0·566	0·515	0·519	3·840
4	0·629	0·561	0·566	0·992	0·567	0·618	3·933
5	0·440	0·504	0·515	0·567	0·932	0·592	3·550
6	0·580	0·537	0·519	0·618	0·592	0·932	3·778
			Girls: $\mathbf{A}_2(n_2 = 86)$				
1	1·108	0·877	0·869	0·684	0·559	0·695	4·792
2	0·877	1·196	0·970	0·791	0·726	0·782	5·342
3	0·869	0·970	1·134	0·793	0·719	0·795	5·280
4	0·684	0·791	0·793	1·019	0·694	0·754	4·735
5	0·559	0·726	0·719	0·694	1·161	0·765	4·624
6	0·695	0·782	0·795	0·754	0·765	1·161	4·952
			Both Sexes: $\mathbf{A}(n = 290)$				
1	1·000	0·717	0·712	0·645	0·475	0·614	4·163
2	0·717	1·000	0·746	0·629	0·570	0·610	4·272
3	0·712	0·746	1·000	0·633	0·575	0·601	4·267
4	0·645	0·629	0·633	1·000	0·605	0·658	4·170
5	0·475	0·570	0·575	0·605	1·000	0·643	3·868
6	0·614	0·610	0·601	0·658	0·643	1·000	4·126

For computational convenience each variate has been scaled so that its variance averaged over the two samples is unity. Hence the pooled covariance matrix **A** has unit diagonal elements.

The hypothesis set up is that two correlated factors are present and that the pattern of loadings is as follows:

$$\begin{matrix} x & x & x & x & 0 & x \\ 0 & 0 & 0 & x & x & x \end{matrix}$$

An approximate analysis of the matrix **A** was first performed using the method of Section 5.5. This gave the following preliminary estimates of the loadings:

$$\begin{matrix} 0{\cdot}86 & 0{\cdot}86 & 0{\cdot}85 & 0{\cdot}34 & 0 & 0{\cdot}19 \\ 0 & 0 & 0 & 0{\cdot}51 & 0{\cdot}80 & 0{\cdot}65 \end{matrix}$$

The correlation coefficient between the two factors was found to be approximately 0·80, and the residual variances were estimated as:

$$\begin{matrix} 0{\cdot}260 & 0{\cdot}260 & 0{\cdot}278 & 0{\cdot}347 & 0{\cdot}360 & 0{\cdot}344 \end{matrix}$$

The iterative procedure was begun with the above values of $\mathbf{L}'$ and $\mathbf{V}$. In the first iteration it was necessary to start by estimating the factor covariance matrices from (8.10), (8.11) and (8.12). The estimates were given by

$$\hat{\mathbf{\Gamma}}_1 = \begin{bmatrix} 0{\cdot}904 & 0{\cdot}724 \\ 0{\cdot}724 & 0{\cdot}931 \end{bmatrix} \quad \hat{\mathbf{\Gamma}}_2 = \begin{bmatrix} 1{\cdot}227 & 0{\cdot}968 \\ 0{\cdot}968 & 1{\cdot}162 \end{bmatrix}$$

$$\hat{\mathbf{\Gamma}} = \begin{bmatrix} 1{\cdot}000 & 0{\cdot}796 \\ 0{\cdot}796 & 1{\cdot}000 \end{bmatrix}$$

The above values were then used for $\mathbf{\Gamma}_1$, $\mathbf{\Gamma}_2$ and $\mathbf{\Gamma}$ in (8.8) and (8.9), enabling better estimates of the loadings to be obtained. In subsequent iterations the calculations of (8.8) to (8.13) were performed in the order given.

In both factors girls appear to be more variable than boys, but in fact, as will be seen later, $\hat{\mathbf{\Gamma}}_1$ and $\hat{\mathbf{\Gamma}}_2$ do not differ significantly. Despite this we have supposed that the population matrices $\mathbf{\Gamma}_1$ and $\mathbf{\Gamma}_2$ are unequal in order to illustrate the estimation procedure. Five iterations were performed, the last of which is given below. The estimates for $\mathbf{L}'$, $\mathbf{V}$, $\mathbf{\Gamma}_1$, $\mathbf{\Gamma}_2$ and $\mathbf{\Gamma}$ were found from the previous iteration.

$$\mathbf{\Gamma}_1 = \begin{bmatrix} 0{\cdot}902 & 0{\cdot}725 \\ 0{\cdot}725 & 0{\cdot}931 \end{bmatrix} \qquad \mathbf{\Gamma}_2 = \begin{bmatrix} 1{\cdot}232 & 0{\cdot}978 \\ 0{\cdot}978 & 1{\cdot}165 \end{bmatrix} \qquad \mathbf{\Gamma} = \begin{bmatrix} 1{\cdot}000 & 0{\cdot}800 \\ 0{\cdot}800 & 1{\cdot}000 \end{bmatrix}$$

$\mathbf{L}$	0·835	0·862	0·857	0·356	0	0·194
	0	0	0	0·487	0·797	0·652
$\mathbf{V}$	0·3028	0·2570	0·2656	0·3587	0·3648	0·3349
$\mathbf{L}'\mathbf{V}^{-1}$	2·758	3·354	3·227	0·992	0	0·579
	0	0	0	1·358	2·185	1·947

$$\mathbf{J} = \begin{bmatrix} 8{\cdot}425 & 0{\cdot}861 \\ 0{\cdot}861 & 3{\cdot}672 \end{bmatrix} \qquad \mathbf{J}^{-1} = \begin{bmatrix} 0{\cdot}12161 & -0{\cdot}02851 \\ -0{\cdot}02851 & 0{\cdot}27902 \end{bmatrix}$$

$$(\mathbf{\Gamma}_1^{-1}+\mathbf{J})^{-1} = \begin{bmatrix} 0{\cdot}09034 & 0{\cdot}01998 \\ 0{\cdot}01998 & 0{\cdot}15725 \end{bmatrix} \qquad (\mathbf{\Gamma}_2^{-1}+\mathbf{J})^{-1} = \begin{bmatrix} 0{\cdot}09404 & 0{\cdot}01780 \\ 0{\cdot}01780 & 0{\cdot}16350 \end{bmatrix}$$

							Row sums
$\mathbf{L}'\mathbf{V}^{-1}\mathbf{A}_1$	7·856	7·837	7·870	6·785	5·471	6·228	42.047
	2·945	2·909	2·904	3·789	3·959	3·947	20·453
$\mathbf{L}\ \mathbf{V}^{-1}\mathbf{A}_2$	9·883	10·798	10·556	8·546	7·428	8·525	55·736
	3·503	4·183	4·196	4·368	4·969	4·956	26·175
$\mathbf{M}'_1$	0·7686	0·7661	0·7690	0·6887	0·5734	0·6415	4·2073
	0·6201	0·6140	0·6139	0·7314	0·7319	0·7451	4·0564
$\mathbf{M}'_2$	0·9918	1·0899	1·0674	0·8814	0·7870	0·8899	5·7074
	0·7487	0·8761	0·8739	0·8663	0·9446	0·9621	5·2717
$\mathbf{M}$	0·8348	0·8621	0·8575	0·7458	0·6367	0·7125	4·6521
	0·6582	0·6917	0·6910	0·7714	0·7950	0·8095	4·4168
$\hat{\mathbf{L}}'$	0·835	0·862	0·858	0·357	0·	0·188	
	0	0	0	0·485	0·795	0·659	

$$\mathbf{Z}_1 = \begin{bmatrix} 83{\cdot}69 & 33{\cdot}29 \\ 33{\cdot}29 & 21{\cdot}48 \end{bmatrix} \qquad \mathbf{Z}_2 = \begin{bmatrix} 110{\cdot}95 & 44{\cdot}43 \\ 44{\cdot}43 & 26{\cdot}44 \end{bmatrix} \qquad \mathbf{Z} = \begin{bmatrix} 91{\cdot}77 & 36{\cdot}60 \\ 36{\cdot}60 & 22{\cdot}95 \end{bmatrix}$$

$$\mathbf{\Gamma}_1^* = \begin{bmatrix} 0{\cdot}9026 & 0{\cdot}7242 \\ 0{\cdot}7242 & 0{\cdot}9315 \end{bmatrix} \qquad \mathbf{\Gamma}_2^* = \begin{bmatrix} 1{\cdot}2326 & 0{\cdot}9774 \\ 0{\cdot}9774 & 1{\cdot}1625 \end{bmatrix} \qquad \mathbf{\Gamma}^* = \begin{bmatrix} 1{\cdot}0005 & 0{\cdot}7993 \\ 0{\cdot}7993 & 1{\cdot}0000 \end{bmatrix}$$

$$\hat{\mathbf{\Gamma}}_1 = \begin{bmatrix} 0{\cdot}902 & 0{\cdot}724 \\ 0{\cdot}724 & 0{\cdot}932 \end{bmatrix} \qquad \hat{\mathbf{\Gamma}}_2 = \begin{bmatrix} 1{\cdot}232 & 0{\cdot}977 \\ 0{\cdot}977 & 1{\cdot}163 \end{bmatrix} \qquad \hat{\mathbf{\Gamma}} = \begin{bmatrix} 1{\cdot}000 & 0{\cdot}799 \\ 0{\cdot}799 & 1{\cdot}000 \end{bmatrix}$$

$\hat{\mathbf{V}}$	0·3028	0·2570	0·2638	0·3606	0·3680	0·3324

When performing these calculations it was convenient to find the ratios

$$c_1 = n_1/n = 204/290 = 0{\cdot}70345,$$
$$c_2 = n_2/n = 86/290 = 0{\cdot}29655.$$

Then $\mathbf{M}'$ and $\mathbf{Z}$ were given by

$$\mathbf{M}' = c_1\mathbf{M}'_1 + c_2\mathbf{M}'_2,$$
$$\mathbf{Z} = c_1\mathbf{Z}_1 + c_2\mathbf{Z}_2.$$

The matrices $\mathbf{M}'_1$ and $\mathbf{M}'_2$ are needed only for calculating the χ^2 criterion of (8.14) by the approximate method. Had this not been the final iteration we should have found $\mathbf{M}'$ more easily and directly, without obtaining $\mathbf{M}'_1$ and $\mathbf{M}'_2$. For we have

$$\mathbf{M}' = \mathbf{W}_1\mathbf{L}'\mathbf{V}^{-1}\mathbf{A}_1 + \mathbf{W}_2\mathbf{L}'\mathbf{V}^{-1}\mathbf{A}_2,$$

where

$$\mathbf{W}_1 = c_1(\mathbf{\Gamma}_1^{-1}+\mathbf{J})^{-1} = \begin{bmatrix} 0{\cdot}06355 & 0{\cdot}01405 \\ 0{\cdot}01405 & 0{\cdot}11062 \end{bmatrix},$$

$$\mathbf{W}_2 = c_2(\mathbf{\Gamma}_2^{-1}+\mathbf{J})^{-1} = \begin{bmatrix} 0{\cdot}02789 & 0{\cdot}00528 \\ 0{\cdot}00528 & 0{\cdot}04849 \end{bmatrix}.$$

Thus for example, the first element in the top row of $\mathbf{M}'$ may be computed as:

$$0{\cdot}06355\times 7{\cdot}856 + 0{\cdot}01405\times 2{\cdot}945 + 0{\cdot}02789\times 9{\cdot}883 + 0{\cdot}00528\times 3{\cdot}503 = 0{\cdot}8348.$$

Though the iterations showed signs of convergence some of the loadings are evidently not very near their final values. However, it seems unlikely that further iterations would materially improve the fit.

For testing the hypothesis made about the factors we have $p = 6$, $k = 2$, $m = 8$, and so the number of degrees of freedom for χ^2 is 24. The approximation of (8.15) was used and gave

$$\log_e(|\hat{\mathbf{C}}_1|/|\mathbf{A}_1|) \approx 0{\cdot}0912,$$
$$\log_e(|\hat{\mathbf{C}}_2|/|\mathbf{A}_2|) \approx 0{\cdot}1168.$$

The multiplying factor for the criterion of (8.14) is approximately 0·979. Hence the value of χ^2 is

$$0{\cdot}979(204\times 0{\cdot}0912 + 86\times 0{\cdot}1168) = 28{\cdot}1.$$

This is not significant.

When the criterion of (8.16) was used to test the hypothesis that $\mathbf{\Gamma}_1 = \mathbf{\Gamma}_2$ a value of 2·54 was found for χ^2 which, with 3 degrees of freedom, is below expectation. Hence the apparent differences in the data between boys and girls are not significant.

For reasons of space the number of variates included in the above example is smaller than would normally be the case in practice. Nevertheless the factors derived from them are meaningful. The first three variates are known to be good measures of cognitive ability of a verbal type, while the fifth variate and to a lesser extent variates four and six are concerned with perception and visualization. In view of this the first factor could be labelled 'verbal-intellectual' and the second 'visualization'. The estimate of 0·8, approximately, of the correlation between the factors is greater than was anticipated; but this may be because the children in our samples form a highly selected group, as they were all attending a psychiatric clinic.

REFERENCES

Aitken, A. C. (1934), Note on selection from a multivariate normal population, *Proc. Edin. Math. Soc.* **4**, 106–110

Box, G. E. P. (1949), A general distribution theory for a class of likelihood criteria, *Biometrika*, **36**, 317–346

Pearson, K. (1912), On the general theory of the influence of selection on correlation and variation, *Biometrika* **8**, 437–443

Thomson, G. H. (1951), *The Factorial Analysis of Human Ability*, 5th ed., London University Press

Thurstone, L. L. (1947), *Multiple Factor Analysis*, University of Chicago Press

APPENDIX

Matrices and Determinants

In this appendix we summarize those definitions and results of matrix algebra and the theory of determinants which are required for an understanding of this book. For proofs of some of the theorems the reader is recommended to refer to standard works on the subject.

A $p \times q$ matrix $\mathbf{A}$ is a rectangular array of numbers, or elements, arranged in p rows and q columns. In full it would be written as

$$\mathbf{A} = \begin{bmatrix} a_{11} & a_{12} & \cdot & \cdot & \cdot & a_{1q} \\ a_{21} & a_{22} & \cdot & \cdot & \cdot & a_{2q} \\ \cdot & \cdot & & & & \cdot \\ \cdot & \cdot & & & & \cdot \\ \cdot & \cdot & & & & \cdot \\ a_{p1} & a_{p2} & \cdot & \cdot & \cdot & a_{pq} \end{bmatrix}.$$

This is usually abbreviated to $\mathbf{A} = [a_{ij}]$, where $i = 1, 2, ..., p$ and $j = 1, 2, ..., q$. Throughout this book we confine our attention to matrices whose elements are real numbers. Capital boldface letters are used to denote matrices. Their elements are denoted by the corresponding lower-case letters with appropriate subscripts.

The sum of two matrices, $\mathbf{A}$ and $\mathbf{B}$, with the same numbers of rows and columns, is defined by

$$\mathbf{A}+\mathbf{B} \equiv [a_{ij}]+[b_{ij}] = [a_{ij}+b_{ij}].$$

The product of a matrix and a real number, or scalar, λ is defined by

$$\lambda\mathbf{A} = \mathbf{A}\lambda = [\lambda a_{ij}].$$

If $\lambda = -1$ the product is written as $-\mathbf{A}$. A null matrix is one whose elements are all zero. If $\mathbf{A}$ is null, we write $\mathbf{A} = 0$. It may be verified that these operations satisfy the laws

$$\mathbf{A}+\mathbf{B} = \mathbf{B}+\mathbf{A},$$

$$(\mathbf{A}+\mathbf{B})+\mathbf{C} = \mathbf{A}+(\mathbf{B}+\mathbf{C}),$$

$$\mathbf{A}-\mathbf{A} = 0,$$

$$(\lambda+\mu)\mathbf{A} = \lambda\mathbf{A}+\mu\mathbf{A},$$

$$\lambda(\mathbf{A}+\mathbf{B}) = \lambda\mathbf{A}+\lambda\mathbf{B}.$$

If **A** has the same number of columns as **B** has rows, it is possible to define the product **AB**. Suppose that $\mathbf{A} = [a_{ij}]$ is of order $p \times q$ and that $\mathbf{B} = [b_{ij}]$ is of order $q \times r$. Then $\mathbf{AB} = \mathbf{C}$ is a matrix of order $p \times r$. The element c_{ik} in the ith row and kth column of **C** is given by

$$c_{ik} = \sum_{j=1}^{q} a_{ij} b_{jk}.$$

It will be noted that this is the sum of products of corresponding elements in the ith row of **A** and the kth column of **B**.

The product **BA** may be meaningless even if **AB** exists. The two products can co-exist only if, for **A** of order $p \times q$, **B** is of order $q \times p$. In this case **AB** is a square matrix of order p while **BA** is a square matrix of order q. Even if $p = q$, and both **A** and **B** are square, it can easily be verified that **AB** is not in general equal to **BA**. We must therefore always distinguish between pre-multiplication and post-multiplication. In **AB**, for example, **A** is post-multiplied by **B** while **B** is pre-multiplied by **A**.

If **A**, **B** and **C** are matrices of order $p \times q$, $q \times r$ and $r \times s$ respectively, it is possible to form the product **AB** and post-multiply it by **C**. The result may be written (**AB**)**C**. We can also find the product **BC** and pre-multiply it by **A** to obtain a matrix **A**(**BC**). From the definition of matrix multiplication it is clear that

$$(\mathbf{AB})\mathbf{C} = \mathbf{A}(\mathbf{BC}).$$

Hence each of these two matrices may be denoted without ambiguity by **ABC**. Similar results hold for products of more than three matrices. In finding such products it is important that the correct order of the matrices should be preserved. For a square matrix **A** it is convenient to write $\mathbf{A}^2 = \mathbf{AA}$, $\mathbf{A}^3 = \mathbf{AAA}$, etc.

It may be noted that matrix multiplication also satisfies the laws

$$\mathbf{A}(\mathbf{B}+\mathbf{C}) = \mathbf{AB}+\mathbf{AC},$$
$$(\mathbf{A}+\mathbf{B})\mathbf{C} = \mathbf{AC}+\mathbf{BC}.$$

Thus matrices obey all the ordinary laws of elementary algebra except the commutative law of multiplication.

The transpose of the $p \times q$ matrix $\mathbf{A} = [a_{ij}]$ is defined to be the $q \times p$ matrix $\mathbf{A}' = [a'_{ij}]$ for which $a'_{ij} = a_{ji}$. Thus the element in the ith row and jth column of $\mathbf{A}'$ is the same as the element in the jth row and ith column of $\mathbf{A}$. The operation of transposition has the properties

$$(\mathbf{A}')' = \mathbf{A},$$
$$(\mathbf{A}+\mathbf{B})' = \mathbf{A}'+\mathbf{B}',$$
$$(\mathbf{AB})' = \mathbf{B}'\mathbf{A}'.$$

For the transpose of the product of more than two matrices the rule is that the transposed matrices are multiplied in reverse order. Thus $(\mathbf{ABC})' = \mathbf{C}'\mathbf{B}'\mathbf{A}'$, $(\mathbf{ABCD})' = \mathbf{D}'\mathbf{C}'\mathbf{B}'\mathbf{A}'$, etc.

Matrices consisting of only one row or column are termed vectors. We use boldface lower-case letters to denote these. For clarity such letters bear a prime if a row vector is intended, but no prime if a column vector is intended. We write, for example,

$$\mathbf{x}' = [x_1 \quad x_2 \dots x_p].$$

When it is necessary to write a column vector in full the elements are put, for convenience, in horizontal alignment, but curled brackets are used to indicate that a vertical alignment is intended. We write, for example,

$$\mathbf{y} = \{y_1 \quad y_2 \dots y_p\}.$$

A 1×1 matrix, which consists of only one element, is merely a scalar. It may occur as the result of post-multiplying a row vector by a column vector with the same number of elements. For example, with $\mathbf{x}'$ and $\mathbf{y}$ as above, we have

$$\mathbf{x}'\mathbf{y} = \mathbf{y}'\mathbf{x} = x_1 y_1 + x_2 y_2 + \dots + x_p y_p.$$

A quantity of this kind is often termed the inner product of the two vectors.

From now on we shall be concerned, unless we state otherwise, with square matrices of the same order p, which can be added and multiplied at will, and with vectors of order p.

The matrix $\mathbf{A}$ is called symmetric if $\mathbf{A} = \mathbf{A}'$, or $a_{ij} = a_{ji}$. It may be noted that a symmetric matrix of order p has in general $\frac{1}{2}p(p+1)$ distinct elements.

A matrix of considerable interest is the unit matrix $\mathbf{I}$. This has unities for its diagonal elements and zeros elsewhere. If it is important to stress the order of the matrix we write it as $\mathbf{I}_p$, but otherwise the suffix is suppressed. The unit matrix satisfies

$$\mathbf{IA} = \mathbf{AI} = \mathbf{A}.$$

The matrix $\mathbf{I}$ is a special case of a diagonal matrix, i.e. a matrix whose non-diagonal elements are all zero.

For any square matrix $\mathbf{A}$ we can define the determinant, written $|\mathbf{A}|$ or $|a_{ij}|$, by

$$|\mathbf{A}| = \sum \pm a_{1\alpha} a_{2\beta} \dots a_{p\nu}$$

where the summation, of $p!$ terms, is over all permutations $\alpha, \beta, \dots, \nu$ of the integers $1, 2, \dots, p$. The sign $+$ or $-$ is prefixed to each term according as the permutation is even or odd. To explain the terms even and odd in this connection we note that the integers $1, 2, \dots, p$, in natural order, may be changed into a different order $\alpha, \beta, \dots, \nu$ by a number of successive transpositions, where a transposition means the interchange in position of two integers. A particular permutation $\alpha, \beta, \dots, \nu$ may be obtained by many different sequences of transpositions, but it can be shown that the number of transpositions required is either always even or always odd. The sign of the corresponding term in the summation is $+$ if the number is even and $-$ if the number is odd.

It can be shown that

$$|\mathbf{A}'| = |\mathbf{A}|$$

and that

$$|\mathbf{AB}| = |\mathbf{BA}| = |\mathbf{A}| \times |\mathbf{B}|.$$

If $\mathbf{A}$ is a diagonal matrix,

$$|\mathbf{A}| = a_{11} a_{22} \dots a_{pp}.$$

A submatrix of $\mathbf{A}$ is a matrix formed from $\mathbf{A}$ by deleting a number of rows and columns. A minor is the determinant of a square submatrix of $\mathbf{A}$. The minor of a_{ij} in $|\mathbf{A}|$ is the determinant of the submatrix of $\mathbf{A}$ formed by deleting the ith row and the jth column. The cofactor of a_{ij} in $|\mathbf{A}|$ denoted by A_{ij}, is $(-1)^{i+j}$ times the minor of a_{ij}. It can be, shown that

$$\sum_k a_{ik} A_{ik} = \sum_k a_{ki} A_{ki} = |\mathbf{A}| \tag{1}$$

and that, if $i \neq j$,

$$\sum_k a_{ik} A_{jk} = \sum_k a_{kj} A_{ki} = 0.$$

If $|\mathbf{A}| = 0$, $\mathbf{A}$ is said to be singular. Let us suppose that $|\mathbf{A}| \neq 0$, i.e. that $\mathbf{A}$ is non-singular, and let us define a matrix $\mathbf{A}^{-1} = [a^{ij}]$ by

$$a^{ij} = A_{ji}/|\mathbf{A}|. \tag{2}$$

Then the above equations may be rewritten

$$\sum_k a_{ik}a^{ki} = \sum_k a^{ik}a_{ki} = 1$$

and, for $i \neq j$,

$$\sum_k a_{ik}a^{kj} = \sum_k a^{ik}a_{kj} = 0.$$

These equations when expressed in terms of matrices become simply

$$\mathbf{AA}^{-1} = \mathbf{A}^{-1}\mathbf{A} = \mathbf{I}.$$

The matrix $\mathbf{A}^{-1}$ is termed the inverse of $\mathbf{A}$. It exists and is uniquely determined provided that $\mathbf{A}$ is non-singular. Since

$$|\mathbf{A}|\,|\mathbf{A}^{-1}| = |\mathbf{AA}^{-1}| = |\mathbf{I}| = 1,$$

we have

$$|\mathbf{A}^{-1}| = 1/|\mathbf{A}|.$$

It is easy to show that $(\mathbf{A}')^{-1} = (\mathbf{A}^{-1})'$. If $\mathbf{A}$ and $\mathbf{B}$ are both non-singular then $(\mathbf{AB})^{-1}$ exists and is equal to $\mathbf{B}^{-1}\mathbf{A}^{-1}$. This is so because

$$(\mathbf{AB})(\mathbf{B}^{-1}\mathbf{A}^{-1}) = \mathbf{A}(\mathbf{BB}^{-1})\mathbf{A}^{-1} = \mathbf{AIA}^{-1} = \mathbf{AA}^{-1} = \mathbf{I}.$$

Similarly, if $\mathbf{A}$, $\mathbf{B}$ and $\mathbf{C}$ are all non-singular,

$$(\mathbf{ABC})^{-1} = \mathbf{C}^{-1}\mathbf{B}^{-1}\mathbf{A}^{-1}.$$

The rule for finding the inverse of the product of any number of matrices is that the inverse matrices must be multiplied together in reverse order. If $\mathbf{D}$ is a diagonal matrix with elements $d_1, d_2, \ldots, d_p$, then $\mathbf{D}^{-1}$ is diagonal with elements $1/d_1$ $1/d_2, \ldots, 1/d_p$.

When p does not exceed 3, results (1) and (2) are useful for the numerical evaluation of $|\mathbf{A}|$ and $\mathbf{A}^{-1}$ respectively. For $p > 3$ the calculation of the cofactors involves too much laborious arithmetic and other more convenient methods become necessary. Some of these will be discussed later.

The cofactor A_{ij} may be regarded as the partial derivative of $|\mathbf{A}|$ with respect to a_{ij}. If each element of $\mathbf{A}$ is a function of a number of quantities $c_1, c_2, \ldots, c_n$, the partial derivative of $|\mathbf{A}|$ with respect to c_k is given by

$$\frac{\partial|\mathbf{A}|}{\partial c_k} = \sum_{i,j} \frac{\partial|\mathbf{A}|}{\partial a_{ij}} \frac{\partial a_{ij}}{\partial c_k} = \sum_{i,j} A_{ij} \frac{\partial a_{ij}}{\partial c_k}. \tag{3}$$

If $\mathbf{A}$ is symmetric and no distinction is made between a_{ij} and a_{ji}, then, since $A_{ij} = A_{ji}$, we have $\partial|\mathbf{A}|/\partial a_{ij} = 2A_{ij}$ when $i \neq j$.

Throughout this paragraph let us suppose that $h \neq i$ and $k \neq j$. Since A_{ij} contains the element a_{hk}, we may speak of the cofactor of a_{hk} in A_{ij}. It is the factor by which a_{hk} is multiplied in the expansion of A_{ij}, and will be denoted by $A_{ij,hk}$. Thus

$$\sum_k a_{hk} A_{ij,hk} = \sum_h a_{hk} A_{ij,hk} = A_{ij}.$$

A result which is used in Chapter 2, and which is a special case of a theorem due to Jacobi, is

$$A_{ij,hk}|\mathbf{A}| = A_{ij}A_{hk} - A_{ik}A_{hj}. \tag{4}$$

For simultaneous linear equations in several variables the notation of matrix algebra is particularly suitable. The set of p equations

$$a_{i1}x_1 + a_{i2}x_2 + \ldots + a_{ip}x_p = c_i \quad (i = 1, 2, \ldots, p)$$

in the p unknown variables $x_1, x_2, \ldots, x_p$ can be written concisely as

$$\mathbf{Ax} = \mathbf{c}.$$

Suppose that $\mathbf{A}$ is non-singular and that $\mathbf{A}^{-1}$ is known. Pre-multiplication by $\mathbf{A}^{-1}$ then gives the solution of the equations in the form

$$\mathbf{x} = \mathbf{A}^{-1}\mathbf{c},$$

and shows that it is unique.

A set of vectors $\mathbf{z}_1, \mathbf{z}_2, \ldots, \mathbf{z}_k$ is said to be linearly independent if there exists no set of scalers, $c_1, c_2, \ldots, c_k$, not all zero, such that

$$\sum_{h=1}^{k} c_h \mathbf{z}_h = 0.$$

A matrix **A**, rectangular or square, is said to be of rank r if the maximum number of linearly independent rows (or columns) is r. Alternatively and equivalently, the rank of **A** is defined to be r if every minor of order $r+1$ formed from **A** is zero and at least one minor of order r is not zero.

It is often necessary to transform one set of variables or coordinates $x_1, x_2, ..., x_p$ into another set $y_1, y_2, ..., y_p$. In general the transformation giving the y's in terms of the x's and the inverse transformation giving the x's in terms of the y's are represented by the respective equations

$$\mathbf{y} = \mathbf{A}\mathbf{x}, \quad \mathbf{x} = \mathbf{A}^{-1}\mathbf{y},$$

where **A** is supposed non-singular.

In many cases both the x's and the y's represent rectangular, or orthogonal, coordinates. Both the transformation and the matrix defining it are then termed orthogonal. An orthogonal matrix **A** satisfies

$$\mathbf{A}\mathbf{A}' = \mathbf{A}'\mathbf{A} = \mathbf{I},$$

and thus

$$\mathbf{A}' = \mathbf{A}^{-1}, \quad \mathbf{A} = (\mathbf{A}')^{-1}.$$

In view of this, an orthogonal transformation is represented by

$$\mathbf{y} = \mathbf{A}\mathbf{x}, \quad \mathbf{x} = \mathbf{A}'\mathbf{y}.$$

It may be noted that

$$\mathbf{y}'\mathbf{y} = (\mathbf{x}'\mathbf{A}')(\mathbf{A}\mathbf{x}) = \mathbf{x}'(\mathbf{A}'\mathbf{A})\mathbf{x} = \mathbf{x}'\mathbf{x}.$$

Considered geometrically this expresses the fact that the square of the distance of a point from the origin remains invariant under a change of coordinate axes.

For an orthogonal matrix **A** we have

$$|\mathbf{A}|^2 = |\mathbf{A}|\,|\mathbf{A}'| = |\mathbf{A}\mathbf{A}'| = 1,$$

and thus $|\mathbf{A}| = \pm 1$. The sign can always be made $+$ by changing, if necessary, the signs of the elements in any row or column of **A**. Such changes clearly do not affect the orthogonality of **A**.

Any orthogonal matrix of order 2 (with determinant $+1$) has the form

$$\begin{bmatrix} \cos\theta & \sin\theta \\ -\sin\theta & \cos\theta \end{bmatrix}.$$

The transformation of coordinates from (x_1, x_2) to (y_1, y_2) represents a rotation through an angle θ.

Let us consider the quadratic form

$$\mathbf{x}'\mathbf{A}\mathbf{x} = \sum_{i,j} a_{ij}x_i x_j,$$

where $\mathbf{A}$ is symmetric. The quadratic form and the matrix $\mathbf{A}$ are called positive definite if for all non-null $\mathbf{x}$, $\mathbf{x}'\mathbf{A}\mathbf{x} > 0$. (If $>$ is replaced by $\geqslant$, they are called either non-negative definite or positive semi-definite.)

The latent roots (sometimes called characteristic roots or eigenvalues) of a matrix $\mathbf{A}$ are the values of λ satisfying

$$|\mathbf{A} - \lambda\mathbf{I}| = 0, \tag{5}$$

which is an equation in λ of degree p. We shall suppose that the latent roots are non-zero and distinct and that they are arranged in order of magnitude. Corresponding to the rth root λ_r there is a column vector $\mathbf{u}_r$ and a row vector $\mathbf{v}'_r$ satisfying

$$\mathbf{A}\mathbf{u}_r = \lambda_r\mathbf{u}_r,$$
$$\mathbf{v}'_r\mathbf{A} = \lambda_r\mathbf{v}'_r.$$

These vectors are the rth latent column and row vectors of $\mathbf{A}$. They are determined but for a scalar factor.

If $\mathbf{A}$ is symmetric, transposition of the first of these two equations shows that the latent row vector is simply the transpose of the latent column vector. For convenience we may choose the scale of each $\mathbf{u}_r$ so that $\mathbf{u}'_r\mathbf{u}_r = 1$, and then

$$\mathbf{u}'_r\mathbf{A}\mathbf{u}_r = \lambda_r\mathbf{u}'_r\mathbf{u}_r = \lambda_r.$$

With the same assumptions as before regarding the λ_r, the vectors $\mathbf{u}_r$ are now uniquely determined apart from possible reversals of signs. It can also be shown that, for $r \neq s$,

$$\mathbf{u}'_r\mathbf{A}\mathbf{u}_s = \mathbf{u}'_r\mathbf{u}_s = 0.$$

In view of the above equations it is clear that, if $\mathbf{A}$ is symmetric, we can find an orthogonal matrix $\mathbf{U}$, whose rth column is $\mathbf{u}_r$, such that the matrix

$$\mathbf{\Lambda} = \mathbf{U}'\mathbf{A}\mathbf{U} \tag{6}$$

is diagonal. The elements of $\mathbf{\Lambda}$ are the latent roots λ_1, λ_2, ..., λ_p. For the numerical evaluation of latent roots and vectors see Chapter 4.

By taking the determinant of the matrix in (6) we obtain

$$|\mathbf{\Lambda}| = |\mathbf{U}'|\,|\mathbf{A}|\,|\mathbf{U}| = |\mathbf{A}|,$$

and thus

$$|\mathbf{A}| = \lambda_1\lambda_2 \ldots \lambda_p.$$

On pre-multiplying in (6) by $\mathbf{U}$ and post-multiplying by $\mathbf{U}'$, we find that

$$\mathbf{A} = \mathbf{U\Lambda U}',$$

and inversion of this gives

$$\mathbf{A}^{-1} = \mathbf{U\Lambda}^{-1}\mathbf{U}'.$$

The last equation may be used to find the inverse of a matrix whose latent roots and vectors are known.

Now consider the orthogonal transformation defined by

$$\mathbf{y} = \mathbf{U}'\mathbf{x}, \quad \mathbf{x} = \mathbf{Uy},$$

with $\mathbf{U}$ as above. For the transformation of the quadratic form $\mathbf{x}'\mathbf{Ax}$ we have

$$\mathbf{x}'\mathbf{Ax} = (\mathbf{y}'\mathbf{U}')\mathbf{A}(\mathbf{Uy}) = \mathbf{y}'(\mathbf{U}'\mathbf{AU})\mathbf{y} = \mathbf{y}'\mathbf{\Lambda y}$$

$$= \sum_{r=1}^{p} \lambda_r y_r^2.$$

If the quadratic form and the matrix $\mathbf{A}$ are positive definite it follows that $\lambda_r > 0$ for all r and conversely.

Suppose that $\mathbf{A}$ is a $p \times q$ matrix and that $\mathbf{B}$ is a $q \times p$ matrix. Then it can be proved that the latent roots of $\mathbf{AB}$ are the same as those of $\mathbf{BA}$, apart from a certain number of zeros when $p \neq q$. This means that the latent roots of $\mathbf{I}_p + \mathbf{AB}$ are the same as those of $\mathbf{I}_q + \mathbf{BA}$ except perhaps for a number of unities. Hence we have

$$|\mathbf{I}_p + \mathbf{AB}| = |\mathbf{I}_q + \mathbf{BA}|. \tag{7}$$

This result is made use of in Chapter 2.

The trace of a matrix $\mathbf{A}$, written tr $\mathbf{A}$, is the sum of its diagonal elements. It may very easily be verified that

$$\operatorname{tr}(\mathbf{A}+\mathbf{B}) = \operatorname{tr}\mathbf{A} + \operatorname{tr}\mathbf{B},$$

$$\operatorname{tr}(\mathbf{AB}) = \operatorname{tr}(\mathbf{BA}).$$

The latter equation holds even when $\mathbf{A}$ and $\mathbf{B}$ are rectangular provided that both products exist. By expansion of equation

(5) it can be seen that the sum of the latent roots of **A** is equal to tr **A**. This result can also be obtained by taking the trace of the matrix in (6), since

$$\text{tr}(\mathbf{\Lambda}) = \text{tr}(\mathbf{U}'\mathbf{A}\mathbf{U}) = \text{tr}(\mathbf{A}\mathbf{U}\mathbf{U}') = \text{tr}(\mathbf{A}\mathbf{I}) = \text{tr}\,\mathbf{A}.$$

Suppose that the matrix $\mathbf{T} = [t_{ij}]$ is such that $t_{ij} = 0$ if $i < j$, i.e. such that all elements above the diagonal are zero. Then **T** is said to be lower triangular. Since $\mathbf{T}'$ has zero elements below the diagonal it is called upper triangular. The product of two lower triangular matrices is also lower triangular. Similarly for upper triangular matrices. The determinant of **T** is given simply by

$$|\mathbf{T}| = t_{11}t_{22} \ldots t_{pp}.$$

The inverse matrix $\mathbf{T}^{-1} = [t^{ij}]$, which is also lower triangular, may be found with great ease by equating corresponding elements on the two sides of the equation

$$\mathbf{T}^{-1}\mathbf{T} = \mathbf{I}.$$

For the diagonal elements we have

$$t^{ii}t_{ii} = 1, \quad \text{i.e. } t^{ii} = 1/t_{ii}, \tag{8}$$

and for the non-diagonal elements,

$$\sum_{k=j}^{i} t^{ik}t_{kj} = 0 \quad (i > j).$$

The last equation may be put in the form

$$t^{ij} = -t^{jj} \sum_{k=j+1}^{i} t^{ik}t_{kj}. \tag{9}$$

Equations (8) and (9) enable us to calculate successively (supposing $p \geqslant 3$)

$$t^{11},\ t^{22},\ t^{21},\ t^{33},\ t^{32},\ t^{31},\ \text{etc.}$$

The inversion of matrices of large order is nowadays usually carried out on electronic computers. For matrices of smaller order the process can be performed quite conveniently with desk calculating machines. We shall discuss briefly certain methods which are suitable for this purpose. Without loss of generality we may assume that the matrix **A** requiring inversion is symmetric. For if **A** is not symmetric, we can invert the symmetric matrix $\mathbf{AA}'$ and then find $\mathbf{A}^{-1}$ as $\mathbf{A}'(\mathbf{AA}')^{-1}$. One way of inverting a matrix is to use the pivotal condensation method of Aitken (1937); but we describe here other methods which are particularly convenient for our purposes and which make use of the properties of triangular matrices.

In this book the matrices which require inversion are both symmetric and positive definite. Let us therefore consider a matrix **A** of this kind. We first express **A** in the form

$$\mathbf{A} = \mathbf{T}\mathbf{T}',$$

where $\mathbf{T} = [t_{ij}]$ is lower triangular with positive diagonal elements. This is done by equating corresponding elements. For the diagonal elements of **A** we obtain

$$\sum_{k=1}^{i} t_{ik}^2 = a_{ii},$$

and for the non-diagonal elements we have

$$\sum_{k=1}^{j} t_{ik}t_{jk} = a_{ij} \quad (i > j).$$

The above equations may be transformed into

$$\left.\begin{aligned} t_{11} &= \sqrt{a_{11}} \\ t_{ii} &= \sqrt{(a_{ii} - \sum_{k=1}^{i-1} t_{ik}^2)} \qquad (i > 1) \end{aligned}\right\} \tag{10}$$

$$\left.\begin{aligned} t_{i1} &= (1/t_{11})a_{i1} \qquad (i > 1) \\ t_{ij} &= (1/t_{jj})(a_{ij} - \sum_{k=1}^{j-1} t_{ik}t_{jk}) \quad (i > j > 1) \end{aligned}\right\} \tag{11}$$

These enable us to calculate successively (supposing $p \geqslant 3$)

$$t_{11},\ t_{21},\ t_{31},\ \ldots,\ t_{22},\ t_{32},\ \ldots,\ t_{33},\ \text{etc.}$$

When $\mathbf{T}^{-1}$ has been found by the method previously described, the inverse of **A** is given by

$$\mathbf{A}^{-1} = (\mathbf{T}^{-1})'\mathbf{T}^{-1}.$$

For the determinant of **A** we have

$$|\mathbf{A}| = |\mathbf{T}|^2 = t_{11}^2 t_{22}^2 \ldots t_{pp}^2.$$

If **A**, though symmetric, is not positive definite, the above method of finding $\mathbf{A}^{-1}$ cannot conveniently be employed since some of the quantities under the square root sign are then negative. We may instead express **A** in the form $\mathbf{T}^*\mathbf{T}'$, where **T** and $\mathbf{T}^*$ are both lower triangular, the latter having unit diagonal elements. Some of the diagonal elements t_{ii} of **T** are negative. The ith column of $\mathbf{T}^*$ is that of **T** multiplied by $1/t_{ii}$. This is, essentially, the Doolittle method. The merit of both methods, particularly the first, is that very few numbers need to be recorded.

REFERENCE

Aitken, A.C. (1937), The evaluation of a certain triple-product matrix, *Proc. Roy. Soc. Edin.* **57**, 172–181

INDEX